Silver Burdett Ginn Science

DISCOVERYWORKS

ASSESSMENT GUIDE

GRADE 5

PERFORMANCE ASSESSMENT

OBSERVATION AND INTERVIEW

SELF-ASSESSMENT

PORTFOLIO ASSESSMENT

WRITTEN REVIEWS AND TESTS

Silver Burdett Ginn
PARSIPPANY, NJ   NEEDHAM, MA
Atlanta, GA   Deerfield, IL   Irving, TX   Santa Clara, CA

CREDITS
Contributing artists
Mee Wha Lee, Barbara Epstein-Eagle, Micheal Biegel,
Cheryl Roberts, Stephen Schudlich

Silver Burdett Ginn
A Division of Simon & Schuster
299 Jefferson Road, P.O. Box 480
Parsippany, NJ 07054-0480

ISBN 0-382-33505-8

1 2 3 4 5 6 7 8 9 10 H   05 04 03 02 01 00 99 98 97 96 95

CONTENTS

To the Teacher 1
Overview of the Assessment Guide 2
Performance Assessment 4
   Performance Checklist Science Process Skills 6
Observation and Interview 7
   Observation Checklist Group Skills 9
   Interview Questionnaire 10
   Observation Checklist Scientific Reasoning Skills 11
Self-Assessment 12
   Self-Assessment Student Checklist 13
   Self-Assessment Group Checklist 14
Portfolio Assessment 15
   Inside My Science Portfolio 17
   Journal Science Portfolio 18
   Science Portfolio Evaluation Sheet 19
Written Reviews and Tests 20

UNIT A

Chapter 1   Investigation 1 Review 21
           Investigation 2 Review 22
           Chapter 1 Test 23

Chapter 2   Investigation 1 Review 25
           Investigation 2 Review 26
           Investigation 3 Review 27
           Chapter 2 Test 28

Chapter 3   Investigation 1 Review 30
           Investigation 2 Review 31
           Chapter 3 Test 32

Chapter 4   Investigation 1 Review 34
           Investigation 2 Review 35
           Chapter 4 Test 36

Performance Assessment Test 38
Administering the Performance Assessment . . 40
Performance Assessment Scoring Rubric 41
Unit A Test 42

UNIT B

Chapter 1   Investigation 1 Review 46
           Investigation 2 Review 47
           Chapter 1 Test 48

Chapter 2   Investigation 1 Review 50
           Investigation 2 Review 51
           Chapter 2 Test 52

Chapter 3   Investigation 1 Review 54
           Investigation 2 Review 55
           Investigation 3 Review 56
           Investigation 4 Review 57
           Chapter 3 Test 58

Chapter 4   Investigation 1 Review 60
           Investigation 2 Review 61
           Investigation 3 Review 62
           Chapter 4 Test 63

Performance Assessment Test 65
Administering the Performance Assessment . . 67
Performance Assessment Scoring Rubric 68
Unit B Test 69

UNIT C

Chapter 1   Investigation 1 Review 73
                   Investigation 2 Review 74
                   Investigation 3 Review 75
                   Chapter 1 Test 76

Chapter 2   Investigation 1 Review 78
                   Investigation 2 Review 79
                   Investigation 3 Review . . . 80
                   Chapter 2 Test 81

Performance Assessment Test 83
Administering the Performance Assessment . . 85
Performance Assessment Scoring Rubric 86
Unit C Test 87

UNIT D

Chapter 1   Investigation 1 Review 91
                   Investigation 2 Review 92
                   Chapter 1 Test 93

Chapter 2   Investigation 1 Review 95
                   Investigation 2 Review 96
                   Chapter 2 Test 97

Chapter 3   Investigation 1 Review 99
                   Investigation 2 Review 100
                   Chapter 3 Test 101

Performance Assessment Test 103
Administering the Performance Assessment . 105
Performance Assessment Scoring Rubric . . . 106
Unit D Test 107

UNIT E

Chapter 1   Investigation 1 Review 111
                   Investigation 2 Review 112
                   Chapter 1 Test 113

Chapter 2   Investigation 1 Review 115
                   Investigation 2 Review 116
                   Investigation 3 Review 117
                   Chapter 2 Test 118

Chapter 3   Investigation 1 Review 120
                   Investigation 2 Review 121
                   Investigation 3 Review 122
                   Investigation 4 Review . . . 123
                   Chapter 3 Test 124

Performance Assessment Test 126
Administering the Performance Assessment . 128
Performance Assessment Scoring Rubric . . . 129
Unit E Test 130

UNIT F

Chapter 1   Investigation 1 Review 134
                   Investigation 2 Review 135
                   Investigation 3 Review 136
                   Chapter 1 Test 137

Chapter 2   Investigation 1 Review 139
                   Investigation 2 Review 140
                   Investigation 3 Review 141
                   Chapter 2 Test 142

Chapter 3   Investigation 1 Review 144
                   Investigation 2 Review 145
                   Investigation 3 Review 146
                   Chapter 3 Test 147

Chapter 4   Investigation 1 Review 149
                   Investigation 2 Review 150
                   Investigation 3 Review 151
                   Chapter 4 Test 152

Performance Assessment Test 154
Administering the Performance Assessment . 156
Performance Assessment Scoring Rubric . . . 157
Unit F Test 158

UNIT G

Chapter 1   Investigation 1 Review 162
                   Investigation 2 Review 163
                   Chapter 1 Test 164

Chapter 2   Investigation 1 Review 166
                   Investigation 2 Review 167
                   Chapter 2 Test 168

Chapter 3   Investigation 1 Review 170
                   Investigation 2 Review 171
                   Chapter 3 Test 172

Performance Assessment Test 174
Administering the Performance Assessment . 176
Performance Assessment Scoring Rubric . . . 177
Unit G Test 178

ANSWERS 182

To the Teacher

The key to evaluating the success of any science program lies in assessment methods that help you and your students measure progress toward instructional goals.

A varied assessment program can

- help you determine which students need more help and where classroom instruction needs to be expanded.
- help you judge how well students understand, communicate, and apply what they have learned.
- provide students with strategies for monitoring their own progress and ways to demonstrate their talents and abilities.

Silver Burdett Ginn **Science DiscoveryWorks** provides a comprehensive assessment package, as shown below.

The *Science DiscoveryWorks* Assessment Package		
Learner Objectives	**Assessments Available in *Science DiscoveryWorks***	**Sources in *Science DiscoveryWorks***
Mastery of content	Observation Written Reviews and Tests Portfolios	TG, AG SE, TG, AG SE, TG. AG
Development of process skills and critical thinking skills	Observation Performance Assessment Portfolios Student Self-Assessment	TG, AG SE, TG, AG SE, TG, AG AG
Development of scientific reasoning skills	Observation	TG, AG
Evaluation of individual or group progress	Portfolios Student Self-Assessment Group Self-Assessment	SE, TG, AG AG TG, AG
Effectiveness of instruction	Written Reviews and Tests Portfolio Assessment Performance Assessment	SE, TG, AG TG, AG SE, TG, AG

KEY: *SE-Student Edition; TG-Teaching Guide; AG-Assessment Guide*

1

Overview of the Assessment Guide

Performance Assessment . . . . Page 4

Purpose: Performance Assessment helps you evaluate the skills and concepts developed through hands-on activities. It allows you to check how well students are developing the process skills and critical thinking skills of science.

Materials Provided

- **Performance Checklist: Science Process Skills** helps you record how well students apply science process skills, such as classifying and measuring, during activities and formal performance tasks.

- **Performance Assessment** pages present one task for each unit that demonstrate students' ability to apply science process skills to that unit's concepts.

- **Administering the Assessment** provides detailed plans for organizing students and moving them through the task.

- **Performance Assessment Scoring Rubric** provides a method for evaluating student performance of the task in relation to stated goals.

Observation and Interview . . . . Page 7

Purpose: Observation and Interview allow you to document the day-to-day development of student understanding. Using checklists allows you to organize and standardize the presentation of this information.

Materials Provided

- **Observation Checklist: Group Skills** gives you a summary of students' abilities to work as part of a group. This checklist can also be customized to allow for observation between pairs (or groups) of students.

- **Interview Questionnaire** is a convenient form to help you record data from one-on-one or group interviews with your students.

- **Observation Checklist: Scientific Reasoning Skills** provides a record of students' progress in demonstrating scientific reasoning and critical thinking skills. This checklist can be used during activities and class discussion.

Self-Assessment . . . . Page 12

Purpose: Self-assessment provides a method for analyzing and evaluating one's own strengths and weaknesses. *Science DiscoveryWorks* provides the following self-assessment tools in this guide.

Materials Provided

- **Self-Assessment: Student Checklist** offers students a way to evaluate their own work by rating themselves on a list of criteria.

- **Self-Assessment: Group Checklist** helps students analyze their group skills as they score themselves on specific criteria.

Portfolio Assessment . . . . Page 15

Purpose: Portfolio assessment provides a way of demonstrating a student's growth and progress over time.

Materials Provided

- **Inside My Portfolio** provides criteria for students to use in selecting work for their portfolios. It also serves as a table of contents for the portfolio.

- **Journal: Science Portfolio** provides students with an opportunity to reflect on and write about their individual portfolio selections.

- **Science Portfolio Evaluation Sheet** provides a method for recording how student portfolios demonstrate growth in different areas, including science process skills, concepts, group skills, and scientific reasoning skills.

Written Reviews and Tests . . . . Page 20

Purpose: Written reviews and tests measure students' understanding and retention of concepts at the end of investigations, chapters, and units.

- **Investigation Reviews** focus on material covered in each investigation through such forms as fill-in-the-blank, concept maps, and diagram completions.

- **Chapter Tests** evaluate students' understanding of chapter concepts and vocabulary.

- **Unit Tests** measure students' understanding and retention of concepts developed over an entire unit.

Performance Assessment

Performance assessment allows you to evaluate how well students apply their scientific knowledge and skills in different contexts and realistic situations. Performance assessment is useful in evaluating students' understanding and their approach to a task. Opportunities for performance assessment are spread throughout **Science DiscoveryWorks** in the *Teaching Guide*, *Student Edition*, and *Assessment Guide*.

Materials Provided in the *Teaching Guide*

- Each hands-on activity ends with a section called **Assess Performance.** Here, under the head Process Skills Checklist, the *Teaching Guide* provides questions to ask to assess how well students have applied the process skills of science.

- There are also opportunities to assess performance more formally at the close of selected investigations and at the end of each chapter.

Materials Provided in the *Student Edition*

- The **Reflect and Evaluate** page at the close of each chapter includes a suggested performance assessment task.

- **Unit Project Links** provide an on-going opportunity for assessing performance.

- Answers, predictions, and observations recorded in the *Science Notebook* provide a concrete record of daily performance.

Materials Provided in this *Assessment Guide*

- Observation Checklist: Process Skills

- Unit-by-Unit Performance Assessment Tasks that include student pages, a page that helps you administer the task, and a scoring rubric.

Suggestions For Using
OBSERVATION CHECKLIST: PROCESS SKILLS

Performance Checklist: Science Process Skills is designed to assess science process skills students use during activities as well as performance assessment tasks. To get the most benefit out of this checklist:

- Preview the *Teaching Guide* to determine which process skills are used in each activity.

- Tailor the checklist for assessing individual students during more than one activity or to assess several groups during a single activity.
- Carry the checklist with you and record as you observe.

Suggestions For Administering
THE *UNIT-BY-UNIT PERFORMANCE ASSESSMENT TASKS*

Each formal performance assessment task is designed to be administered at the end of a unit. Each task requires students to use science process skills and unit concepts. Many of the tasks involve teamwork.

Before Administering the Performance Assessment Task

- Check the **Administering the Assessment** page for directions and any materials needed. Set up stations, if necessary.

- Review the **Scoring Rubric**. These rubrics, customized to each unit's performance task, provide one way of quantifying your evaluation of student results. You may wish to distribute this rubric to each group before they begin the assessment task. In this way, they will understand how they will be assessed on their performance.

- Provide a copy of the **Student Recording Pages** to each student or group. These two pages contain student instructions for completing the performance assessment task. You may wish to have students record the names of all group members on each sheet.

During the Performance Assessment

- Consider using the **Performance Assessment: Science Process Skills Checklist** and **Observation Checklist: Group Skills** as you observe students working on the task. These checklists will give you a convenient place to record student's use of process skills and their proficiency at group work.

Assessing Performance

- **Sample responses** for each question included on the **Student Recording Pages** are printed in the answer pages at the back of this guide. Use the **Scoring Rubric** to evaluate student performance based upon observation, the student recording pages, or both.

- In addition, you may wish to have students rate their own work, using the **Scoring Rubric** and/or the **Group Skills Checklist**.

Performance Checklist
Science Process Skills

Student	Observing	Classifying	Measuring/Using Numbers	Communicating	Inferring	Predicting	Collecting/Recording/Interpreting Data	Identifying/Controlling Variables	Defining Operationally	Making Hypotheses	Experimenting	Making/Using Models

Scoring Rubric
3   Demonstrates understanding of skill
2   Demonstrates partial understanding of skill
1   Does not demonstrate understanding of skill

Observation
and Interview

Observing students as they work enables you to form a more complete picture of their progress. Holding interviews with your students, either individually or as a group, in which you ask them to talk about their work helps you to evaluate whether students are able to apply science skills and concepts. Based on what you see and hear, you can adjust your instructional approach by taking into account students' interests and attitudes as well as their strengths and weaknesses. At the same time, you are providing a model that encourages students to acquire and appreciate observation as an important science process skill. *Science DiscoveryWorks* provides you with a variety of checklists so you can customize your observation and interview assessments.

Suggestions For Using
OBSERVATION CHECKLIST: GROUP SKILLS

This checklist notes several categories—both positive and negative—that will help you evaluate how your students work in a group.

- Check a category to indicate that a student demonstrates the behavior, or develop your own rating scale to indicate strengths and weaknesses of your students as they work in groups.

- Use this checklist during group activities and whenever your students work together on unit projects. Remember that each group member is responsible for knowing what other members have contributed toward the success of an activity.

Suggestions For Using
INTERVIEW QUESTIONNAIRE

This questionnaire is a convenient tool to record students' answers to questions that you ask about their work.

- Use in an interview with individual students or use with groups. Responses will help you evaluate how well students understand and apply science skills and concepts. The generic questions are fundamental to the interview technique in science. Use these questions as examples, tailoring additional questions to student responses.

Suggestions For Using
SCIENTIFIC REASONING SKILLS CHECKLIST

The American Association for the Advancement of Science has identified certain attitudes associated with learning as "scientific reasoning skills" that can be used as benchmarks for acquiring science literacy. ***Science DiscoveryWorks*** is designed to foster the following scientific reasoning skills:

1. *Longing to know and understand* the desire to probe, find information, and seek explanations
2. *Questioning of scientific assumptions* the tendency to hold open assumptions, findings, and ideas for further verification
3. *Search for data and its meaning* the propensity to collect information and to analyze it in context
4. *Demand for verification* the inclination to repeat and replicate findings and studies
5. *Respect for logic* the inclination to move from assumptions to testing and from data collection to conclusions
6. *Consideration of premises* the tendency to put into context the reason for a particular point of view
7. *Consideration of consequences* the tendency to put into perspective the results of a particular point of view
8. *Respect for historical contributions* the inclination to understand and learn from the contributions of historical ideas, previous studies, and earlier events

Observation Checklist: Scientific Reasoning Skills will help you keep a record of when students demonstrate the values, attitudes, and skills that go hand in hand with effective science performance.

• The checklist can be customized for assessing an individual student's performance on more than one activity or the responses of the class on one activity.

• Questions in the *Teaching Guide,* indicated by the symbol ▨ can be used as models to apply to non-textbook situations, such as additional activities and the discussion of results.

Observation Checklist
Group Skills

Student	Encourages and Listens to Others	Participates in Discussion	Communicates Clearly	Shares Tasks	Takes Initiative	Shares Responsibility/ Accountability	Does Not Cooperate With Others	Does Not Participate in Discussion

Scoring Rubric	3	Demonstrates excellent group skills
	2	Demonstrates satisfactory group skills
	1	Does not demonstrate satisfactory group skills

Name(s) _____ Date _____

Interview
Questionnaire
....

When students are working in groups:

What do you think about what_____said? _____

_____

What do others think? _____

_____

Can you explain this in a different way? _____

_____

When students are working individually or in groups:

How did you get your result?_____

_____

If you did this activity again, would you get the same result? _____

Why or why not?_____

_____

What data proves that your result is accurate? _____

_____

What would happen if you made some changes? What changes
could be made? What would the results be? _____

_____

Is your result the same as others'? If not, how is it different? _____

How can you explain the differences? _____

_____

What ideas that you already learned were helpful as you
worked on this activity?_____

Observation Checklist
Scientific Reasoning Skills

Student	Longing to Know and Understand	Questioning of Scientific Assumptions	Search for Data and Its Meaning	Demand for Verification	Respect for Logic	Consideration of Premises	Consideration of Consequences	Respect for Historical Contributions

Scoring Rubric

3   Demonstrates development of Scientific Reasoning skills
2   Demonstrates partial development of Scientific Reasoning skills
1   Does not demonstrate development of Scientific Reasoning skills

Self-Assessment

Effective self-assessment can build students' confidence and skills and give them a sense of control over their own learning. **Science DiscoveryWorks** provides two self-assessment checklists for students to use to evaluate their own work as well as the work of groups in which they take part.

Suggestions For Using
SELF-ASSESSMENT: STUDENT CHECKLIST

- **Self- Assessment: Student Checklist** should be distributed after completing an activity. Review the statements and the rating system. Explain that the checklists will not be used to establish grades but are meant to help each person find out more about herself or himself.

- Ask students to think about what they did and what they learned in the activity. Encourage them to rate themselves honestly, emphasizing that there are no "right" answers.

- You may discover that some students are more critical of themselves than they need to be. Consider tailoring the *Self-Assessment: Student Checklist* for students to use as they observe others. Students may get more positive feedback of their own performance than they would give themselves.

Suggestions For Using
SELF-ASSESSMENT: GROUP CHECKLIST

- **Self-Assessment: Group Checklist** can be used for specified cooperative learning activities.

- Model use of the checklist during an activity to give students some idea of what to look for.

- In future activities, suggest that group members take turns being the evaluator.

Name _____ Date _____

Self-Assessment
Student Checklist

....

Give yourself a score for your work. Circle
the number that best describes how you did.
Then complete the sentences on the rest of
the page.

	I can do better.	I was good at this.	I did very well.
1. I followed instructions.	1	2	3
2. I asked questions when I didn't understand.	1	2	3
3. I worked well on my own.	1	2	3
4. I respected the contributions of others.	1	2	3

5. What did I learn from this activity? _____

_____

6. What did I have trouble with? _____

_____

7. How did I contribute to the success of my group? _____

_____

8. I could do better at _____

_____

9. I was best at _____

_____

Self-Assessment
Group Checklist

Give your group work a score. Circle the number that best describes how you think you did. Then complete the sentences at the bottom of the page.

Students in Our Group _____ _____

_____ _____ _____

_____ _____ _____

	We could do better.	We did well enough.	We did extremely well.
1. We prepared for the activity.	1	2	3
2. We carried out our plans.	1	2	3
3. We listened to each other's ideas and suggestions.	1	2	3
4. We worked out our problems together.	1	2	3

5. The biggest problem in the group was _____

_____

6. Our group was best at_____

_____

7. We could do better at_____

_____

8. Our group would like to learn more about _____

_____

14

Portfolio Assessment

A portfolio gives students the opportunity to showcase their best efforts in a collection of their work. Unlike a test, which gives a picture of students' achievements at one certain point, a portfolio provides evidence of progress over time. A portfolio can also

- give insight into students' views of themselves through the specific pieces they choose to include.

- enable you to better communicate with family members about a student's work.

- encourage students to join with you in assessing their work.

- provide a tool for evaluating instruction and curriculum.

Suggestions For Using
PORTFOLIO ASSESSMENT

- Throughout the school year, students can compile a working portfolio for works in progress. There are many suggestions in the *Teaching Guide* for adding to the portfolio.

- On a daily basis, students can review and assess their own progress as they record data and observations on the pages of their *Science Notebooks*.

- At the end of each chapter in the *Student Edition* on the Reflect and Evaluate page, there are suggestions for portfolio pieces that can be used as part of the on-going assessment of student progress.

- At specified times, such as the end of a grading period or the end of one or more units, students should review what they have put into their working portfolios in order to select what they want to include in a display portfolio of finished products.

- The items that go into a display portfolio should be carefully chosen. A display portfolio generally contains examples of required work. It might also include creative work, such as experimental data, original models, stories, and essays.

Suggestions For Using
INSIDE MY SCIENCE PORTFOLIO, SCIENCE PORTFOLIO EVALUATION SHEET, AND JOURNAL: SCIENCE PORTFOLIO

- *Inside My Science Portfolio* helps students select, organize, and evaluate their pieces of work.

- The *Science Portfolio Evaluation Sheet* helps you determine how a portfolio's contents demonstrate growth in different areas of science.

- *Journal: Science Portfolio* gives students the chance to reflect on and write about the selections in their display portfolios.

Suggestions For Implementing
PORTFOLIO ASSESSMENT

Developing Guidelines

- Help students understand what a portfolio is and what they will do to build their own portfolios. Help them list the requirements, such as Chapter Tests and Unit Performance Assessments. Then discuss some of the other kinds of work they might decide to include.

- Develop guidelines for selecting portfolio items. Determine how many items should be included. Also, talk about choosing quality over quantity.

- Set aside certain times for students to work on their portfolios. This may be a few minutes at the end of each investigation, chapter, or unit when students can look over their work and decide if they want to save anything for their display portfolios.

Selecting Pieces for the Display Portfolio

- ***Inside My Science Portfolio*** provides students a place to list, date, and explain the inclusion of each piece.

- ***Journal: Science Portfolio*** Allows students to record in more detail their thoughts about each chosen piece in their display portfolio. You might ask for volunteers to share what they have written in their portfolio journal. Collect the journals from time to time for review.

Evaluating Portfolios

- Decide at what points you want to evaluate students' display portfolios. A logical evaluation checkpoint might be the end of every unit.

- ***Science Portfolio Evaluation Sheet*** aids you in documenting growth in each of the four areas listed on the form.

- Meet with students to hear their own evaluations of their portfolio items. Have some leading statements prepared, such as:

  Show me something you are proud of and explain why.

  Show me something you revised.

  Show me something you enjoyed doing and tell why.

- Let students know if you plan to use the portfolios during conferences with family members, other teachers, or school administrators.

Name _____ Date _____

Inside My
Science Portfolio
··

My Work   *Why I Kept It*

1. _____   _____

   _____

2. _____   _____

   _____

3. _____   _____

   _____

4. _____   _____

   _____

5. _____   _____

   _____

6. _____   _____

   _____

7. _____   _____

   _____

8. _____   _____

   _____

9. _____   _____

   _____

Name_____ Date_____

Journal
Science Portfolio
··

Title_____

Why did I keep it? _____
_____

Why do I want to share this? _____
_____
_____

What does this show about what I have learned? _____
_____
_____

If I did this again, I would do it this way:_____
_____
_____

What surprised me when I did this work? _____
_____
_____

This means something to me because_____
_____
_____

Student_____ Date_____

Science Portfolio
Evaluation Sheet

Growth Area	How Portfolio Demonstrates Growth
Science Concepts	
Science Process Skills and Critical Thinking Skills	
Scientific Reasoning Skills	
Individual or Group Skills	

Summary: _____

_____

Additional Comments: _____

_____

Written Reviews and Tests

Science DiscoveryWorks provides you with quality written assessment tools for each investigation, chapter, and unit that can be made part of an overall assessment plan for your science program. Together with options for performance assessment and portfolio assessment, the written tests and reviews help both teachers and students evaluate growth in understanding science concepts and in developing the skills of science.

In the *Student Edition* and *Teaching Guide*

- In the **Think It/Write It** questions at the end of each investigation, students review their understanding of the major concepts of the investigation.

- In the **Reflect and Evaluate** page at the end of each chapter, students review key vocabulary words, analyze information, and solve problems.

In this *Assessment Guide*

- **Investigation Reviews** Used in conjunction with the Think It/Write It questions in the *Student Edition,* these reviews provide a snapshot of student comprehension. The first two activities help you evaluate how well students understand the content of the investigation. The third activity requires students to apply one of the process skills they used in hands-on activities.

- **Chapter Tests** provide a two-page test at the end of each chapter that complements the Reflect and Evaluate page in the *Student Edition.* The ten questions, presented in a variety of test formats, seek to assess students' understanding of chapter concepts and vocabulary, as well as to provide opportunities to analyze visual information and solve problems.

- **Unit Tests** provide a means of reviewing or testing students' understanding of unit concepts. Each unit test consists of twenty questions in a variety of test formats.

Answers to all written reviews and tests are located at the back of this *Assessment Guide.*

Investigation Review
What Are the Parts of a Flowering Plant?

INVESTIGATION **1**

CHAPTER 1

Name _____ Date _____

1. Use the words in the box to correctly label the plant.

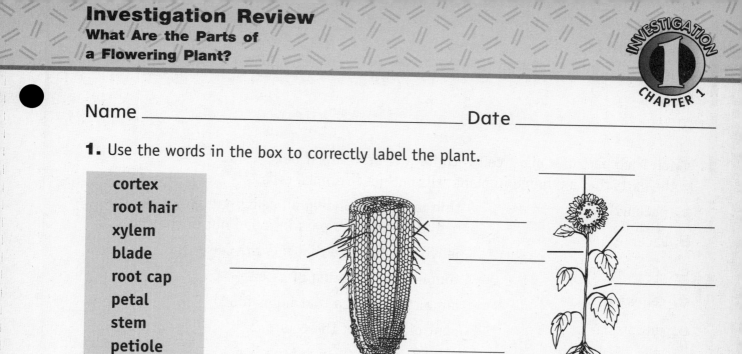

| cortex |
| root hair |
| xylem |
| blade |
| root cap |
| petal |
| stem |
| petiole |

2. a. Complete the chart about plant parts.

Main Plant Parts

Part	Job	Examples
a. _____	• anchor the plant • absorb _____ • store food	Grasses have _____ roots. Carrots have _____.
b. _____	• support leaves and flowers • transport _____	_____, like an oak nonwoody, like a buttercup
c. _____	• make _____ • _____ transport water • allow gases to be exchanged	broad leaf, like a maple _____, like a pine
d. _____	• reproductive parts of plant • pollinated by insects and birds	tulip, black-eyed Susan

b. List three examples of plant parts that you eat or use daily.

_____

Process Skills
Inferring

How might the roots of a dandelion be different from the roots of a grass? Write your answer on a separate sheet of paper.

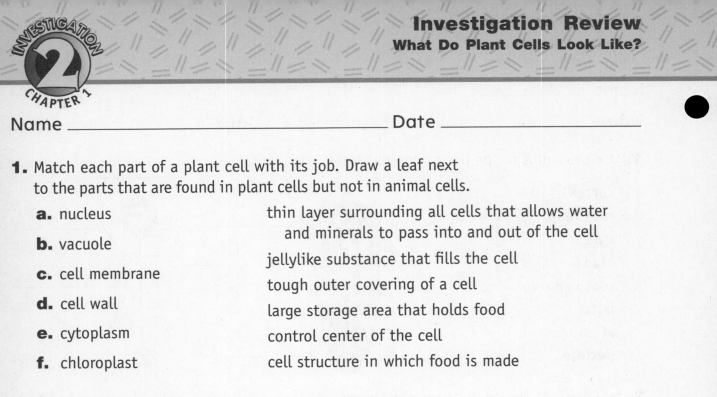

Name _____ Date _____

1. Match each part of a plant cell with its job. Draw a leaf next
to the parts that are found in plant cells but not in animal cells.

a. nucleus

b. vacuole

c. cell membrane

d. cell wall

e. cytoplasm

f. chloroplast

thin layer surrounding all cells that allows water
and minerals to pass into and out of the cell

jellylike substance that fills the cell

tough outer covering of a cell

large storage area that holds food

control center of the cell

cell structure in which food is made

2. Complete the chart about the parts of a tree trunk.

Tree Trunk Parts	
Part	**Description**
_____	Most of a tree's wood is made up of these living xylem cells.
outer bark	_____
_____	The thin growing layer of cells that produces phloem cells and xylem cells
annual rings	_____
_____	The innermost part of a tree made up of old, dried-up layers of xylem

Process Skills
Observing

Suppose you are looking at part of a leaf
through a microscope as shown here.
What is the dark outline that surrounds
each cell?

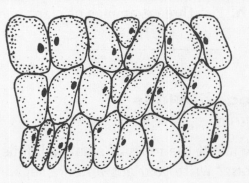

_____

Name _____ Date _____

Analyze Information

1. Jessie placed a white-flowered plant with the roots attached in a vase of water. She added a few drops of red food coloring. Using arrows, show how the red water traveled through the plant. Name, in order, the plant structures it went through.

_____

_____

_____

2. A scientist calculated that if the roots from one rye grass plant were laid end to end, they would be 387 miles (623 km) long. Why do plants have so many roots?

_____

_____

3. In the bowl draw three plant foods that you eat. Label each with the plant part it comes from.

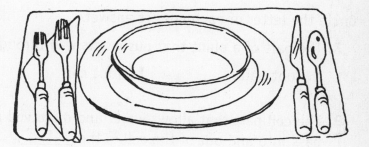

Problem Solving

4. Have you ever see "strings" of celery? What kind of cells do you think the strings are made of? What is their job?

_____

_____

Name _____ Date _____

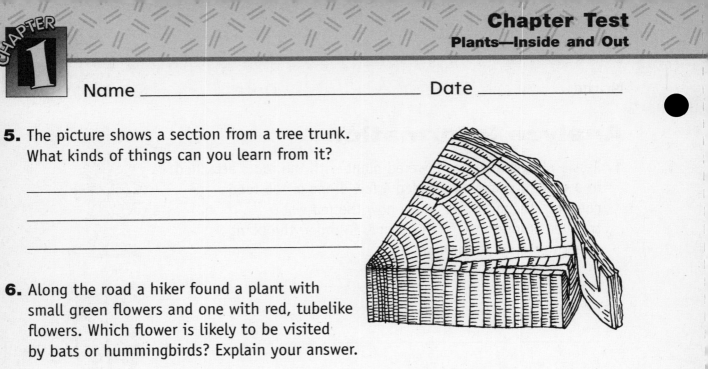

5. The picture shows a section from a tree trunk. What kinds of things can you learn from it?

_____

_____

_____

6. Along the road a hiker found a plant with small green flowers and one with red, tubelike flowers. Which flower is likely to be visited by bats or hummingbirds? Explain your answer.

_____

_____

_____

_____

Word Power

Circle the letter of each correct answer.

7. The part of a plant that pushes its way through soil is the _____.

   a. root hair   **b.** root cap   **c.** xylem   **d.** phloem

8. The cell part that allows water and dissolved minerals to pass into and out of the cell is the _____.

   a. cell membrane   **b.** cytoplasm   **c.** nucleus   **d.** cytoplasm

9. The plant part that protects a tree from disease is _____.

   a. heartwood   **b.** sapwood   **c.** bark   **d.** cambium

10. The part of a plant that anchors it and absorbs moisture is the _____.

   a. stem   **b.** flower   **c.** leaf   **d.** root

Name _____ **Date** _____

1. Use the letters of the terms in the box to label the food chain shown.

> **a.** producer
> **b.** first-order consumer
> **c.** second-order consumer
> **d.** decomposer

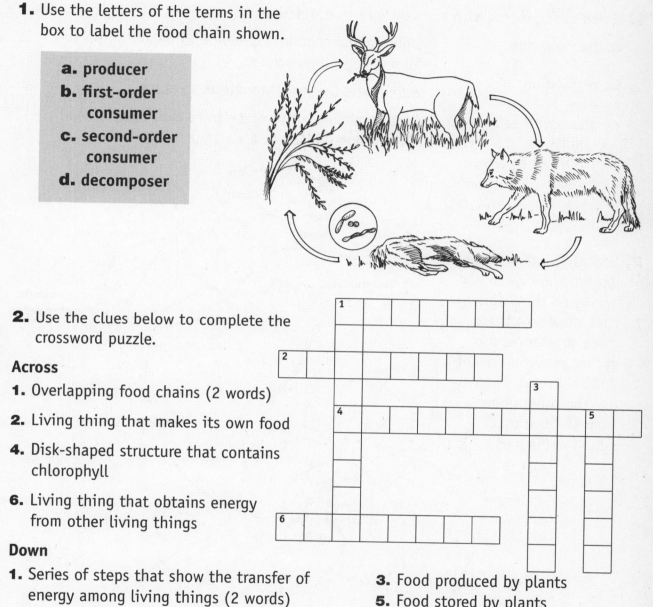

2. Use the clues below to complete the crossword puzzle.

Across

1. Overlapping food chains (2 words)

2. Living thing that makes its own food

4. Disk-shaped structure that contains chlorophyll

6. Living thing that obtains energy from other living things

Down

1. Series of steps that show the transfer of energy among living things (2 words)

3. Food produced by plants

5. Food stored by plants

Process Skills
Making a Hypothesis

On a field trip, you discover a plant with a large, round underground structure about the size of an apple. On a separate sheet of paper, hypothesize whether animals might use it for food. How would you test your hypothesis?

CHAPTER 2

INVESTIGATION 2

Name _____ Date _____

1. Match each process with the sentence that describes it.

   a. transpiration

   b. respiration

   c. photosynthesis

   Light energy combines carbon dioxide and water to form glucose and oxygen.

   Water exits the leaf through its stomata.

   Food combines with oxygen in cells to release energy, with carbon dioxide as a waste product.

2. Near the words *carbon dioxide* and *oxygen* add arrows on the diagram that show how these three substances are cycled between a plant and an animal. Then use the three terms from 1 above to label the diagram.

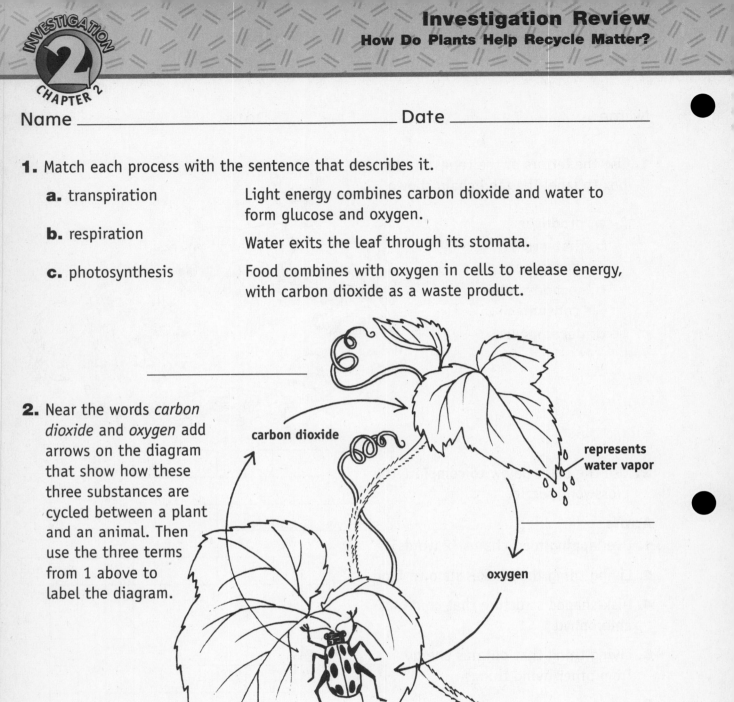

carbon dioxide

represents water vapor

oxygen

Process Skills
Inferring

Suppose you grow a plant for Dawn's birthday gift. The plant is healthy and the soil is fairly dry. You put a plastic bag over the plant when you take it to her party. When Dawn opens the bag, there are droplets inside the bag. What are the droplets? How did they get there? Write your answer on a separate sheet of paper.

Investigation Review
How Do Plants React to
Light and Gravity?

INVESTIGATION **3** CHAPTER 2

Name _____ Date _____

1. Next to each term, list the letter(s) of plants that show an *obvious* tropic response.

geotropism _____

hydrotropism _____

phototropism _____

thigmotropism _____

2. What plant response does each of these "equations" represent?

a. 🌎 + tropism

= _____

b. ☀ + tropism

= _____

c. 🏞 + tropism

= _____

Process Skills
Inferring

Some watermelon seeds were thrown into a compost pile and covered with grass clippings. Explain, on a separate sheet of paper, how a watermelon plant could grow there and where its roots were.

Chapter 2

Name _____   Date _____

Analyze Information

1. Shade in the part of the pie graph that shows the gas that plants produce during photosynthesis.

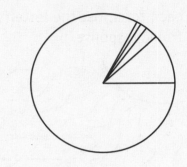

2. Luci put a handful of basil seeds into a pot of soil and watered them. She placed the pot two feet from the only window in her room. Five days later, three little plants started to show. She watered them again. After three days there were five plants, ranging from 3 to 6 inches tall. The plants were bent a little. On a separate sheet of paper draw how you think they might have looked. Explain your drawing.

_____

3. Greg placed a stick in a pot with a young morning glory plant. Draw what will happen after the tendril touches the stick.

Problem Solving

4. In a field, a scientist counted about 6 million grasses and weeds; 700,000 tiny first-order consumers like insects; 350,000 spiders, and other second-order consumers; and only 3 third-order consumers like birds. Draw a pyramid showing this information. Put the producers on the bottom. Why are there so many plants and so few animals? What important part of the food web is missing? Which organisms belong to this part?

_____

_____

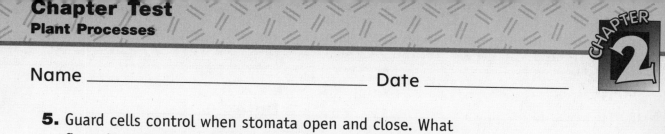
Name _____ Date _____

5. Guard cells control when stomata open and close. What flows in and out of the stomata? What is different on hot days? at night?

_____

_____

_____

6. Name the processes by which each of these living things gets its energy.

_____

_____

_____

Word Power

Circle the letter of each correct answer.

7. A living thing that breaks down the bodies of dead organisms is a _____.

    a. producer   **c.** second-order consumer

    b. first-order consumer   **d.** decomposer

8. Which of the following would best show the feeding relationships among all the living things in a marsh?

    a. a food chain   **b.** a food web   **c.** the oxygen cycle   **d.** the carbon-dioxide cycle

9. The release of water through the stomata of a plant's leaves is _____.

    a. phototropism   **b.** photosynthesis   **c.** respiration   **d.** transpiration

10. A tiny young plant's roots are growing downward. This plant response is known as _____.

    a. geotropism   **b.** phototropism   **c.** thigmotropism   **d.** hydrotropism

© Silver Burdett Ginn

Name _____ Date _____

1. Use the words in the box to label the parts of the tulip.

anther
pistil
stamen
petal
ovary
stigma

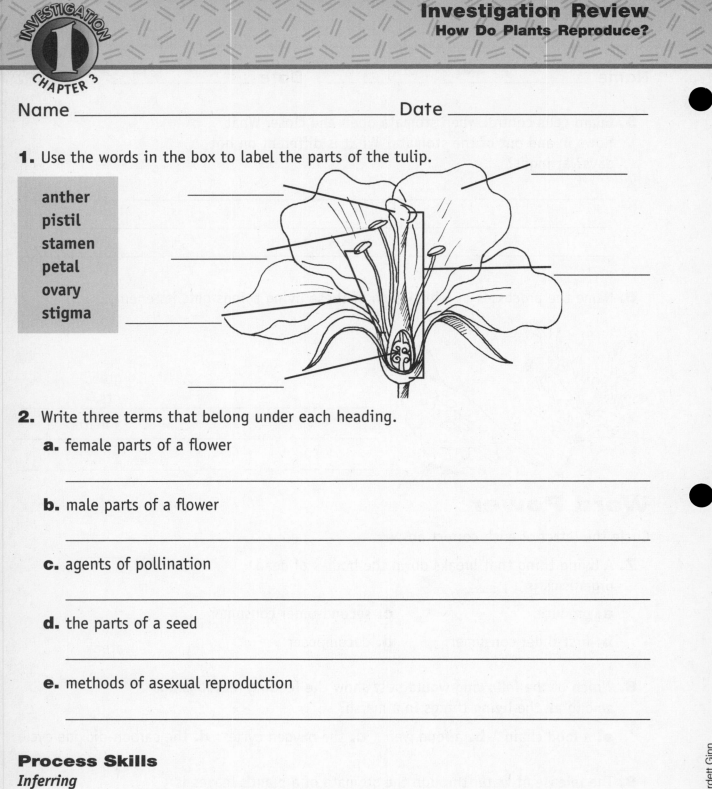

2. Write three terms that belong under each heading.

a. female parts of a flower

_____

b. male parts of a flower

_____

c. agents of pollination

_____

d. the parts of a seed

_____

e. methods of asexual reproduction

_____

Process Skills
Inferring

In northern Canada, a 10,000-year old Arctic lupine seed sprouted!
Many seeds stay in a resting stage until conditions are right for germination. What might you infer about the coverings of these long-
living seeds?

_____

Investigation Review
What Are the Stages in the Life Cycle of a Seed Plant?

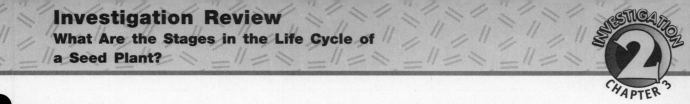

Name _____ Date _____

1. Read the steps that describe the life of an oak tree.
Number the steps in the correct order.

_____   The stem appears above the ground and the seedling develops true oak leaves.

_____   Each year the oak gets taller and has a larger diameter and thicker bark. Now it is considered a tree.

_____   An acorn of an oak tree falls to the ground.

_____   After growing for several seasons, the oak plant develops thicker bark. Now it is called a sapling.

_____   As the acorn germinates, the embryo begins to grow. Roots grow into the soil and absorb water and nutrients.

_____   When this oak develops acorns of its own, it is a mature tree.

2. Write the extreme environmental condition in which the plants with the adaptations listed below could survive.

a. a tree with pine cones that open only at extremely high temperatures

_____

b. a fruit tree with seeds covered with icicles

_____

c. a plant with thick stems that can store thousands of kilograms of water

_____

Process Skills
Communicating, Inferring

Suppose you are planning to study the growth of a desert plant that normally grows to be 100 years old. About how often would you measure the growth of its stem? Infer the rate of growth of such a plant.

_____

_____

Name _____ Date _____

Analyze Information

1. An orchid from Thailand has been produced by means of tissue culture. How does this orchid compare to its parent plant? What are the advantages of using tissue cultures to reproduce plants?

_____

_____

2. People are greatly concerned when a wildfire destroys thousands of acres of forests. Yet some trees depend on fire for their reproduction. Explain why.

_____

_____

3. Where is the pictured plant best adapted to live? Explain your answer.

_____

_____

_____

4. What will happen to a carrot top that is suspended in a jar of water after a week or more? What kind of reproduction is this?

_____

Problem Solving

5. Suppose you could shrink down to the size of a bee. Draw how you would fly around these apple blossoms in order to help the apple tree reproduce. Place an X in the spot where seeds will form.

Name _____ Date _____

6. The stages in the development of a soybean plant are shown.
Number the stages correctly. Circle and label the plant's
first true leaves. Label the germinating seed and the seedling.

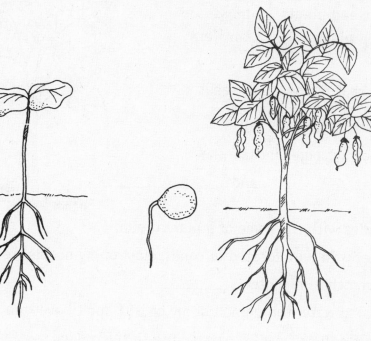

Word Power

Circle the letter of each correct answer.

7. Which of the following plant processes does a hummingbird
help a plant with directly?

   a. germination   **b.** pollination   **c.** adaptation   **d.** fertilization

8. The part of a seed that is the baby plant is the _____.

   a. embryo   **b.** seed coat   **c.** stored food   **d.** stamen

9. The _____ protects the seed from injury.

   a. stamen   **b.** seed leaves   **c.** ovule   **d.** seed coat

10. When a male sex cell joins a female sex cell, _____ occurs.

   a. pollination   **c.** fertilization

   b. vegetative propagation   **d.** germination

INVESTIGATION
1
CHAPTER 4

Name _____ Date _____

1. Use the diagram and the words in the box to complete the sentences.

ferns	nonseed plants	mosses
horsetails	seed plants	conifers

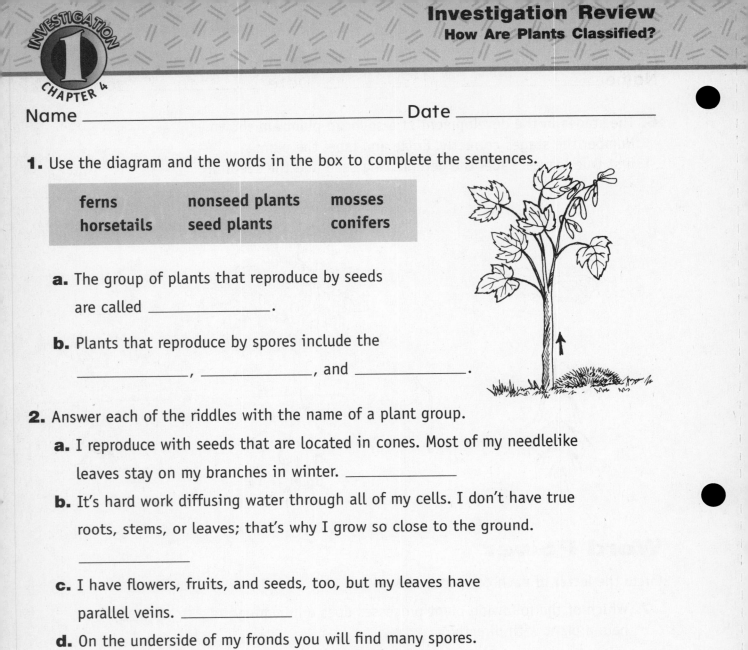

a. The group of plants that reproduce by seeds

are called _____.

b. Plants that reproduce by spores include the

_____, _____, and _____.

2. Answer each of the riddles with the name of a plant group.

a. I reproduce with seeds that are located in cones. Most of my needlelike

leaves stay on my branches in winter. _____

b. It's hard work diffusing water through all of my cells. I don't have true

roots, stems, or leaves; that's why I grow so close to the ground.

_____

c. I have flowers, fruits, and seeds, too, but my leaves have

parallel veins. _____

d. On the underside of my fronds you will find many spores.

My underground stems are called rhizomes. _____

Process Skills
Classifying

Suppose you go into Meg's Flower Shop. You see roses, arranged
with ferns. You notice that there are mosses growing in the geranium pots. Based on what you have learned about plants, why is
"Meg's Flower Shop" not an accurate name for the shop? Classify
all the plants you see in the shop.

_____

_____

Name _____ Date _____

1. Circle the word that best completes each sentence.

a. To conserve water, some plants have wax coatings on their (roots, **leaves**).

b. Some desert plants have long (**roots**, stems) that spread out in all directions beneath the soil's surface.

c. The (roots, **stems**) of some desert plants store tremendous amounts of water.

d. To keep from becoming waterlogged, a water lily has stomata on the (underside, **tops**) of its leaves.

e. In the winter, (coniferous, **deciduous**) trees shed all their leaves and go through a "resting" period.

2. What does each of the following groups of terms have in common?

a. deforestation, pollution, habitat destruction

_____

b. wind, water, animals, seeds

_____

c. cold temperatures, little rainfall, permafrost

_____

Process Skills
Predicting

Two hikers collected brightly colored leaves that had fallen to the forest floor in autumn. They left these leaves on a table. Predict what changes, if any, you would see in the leaves after three days.

_____

_____

Analyze Information

1. Circle the compound leaf. How are the other leaves alike?

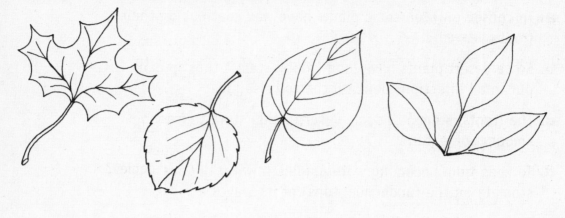

_____

2. Jacob is watering a dish garden. In it are some lilies and a fern. Part of the soil is covered with moss. How does each plant take up water?

_____

_____

3. How do you think the seeds of the plant at right get from place to place?

_____

_____

_____

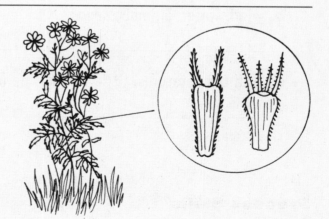

Problem Solving

4. How do plants that live high in the rain forest trees get water?

_____

_____

Name _____ Date _____

5. Suppose you notice that the habitat of a field near your school is being destroyed. There is a new manufacturing plant nearby and you think the pollution from the plant may be affecting the field and the environment near your school. You decide to write some letters about the problem. On another sheet of paper, explain whom you would write to, and what you would say in your letters.

6. Extinction is a natural process. Why then are so many people concerned about endangered species today? What are some things that you can do to help prevent the loss of plant species?

_____

_____

_____

_____

_____

Word Power

Circle the letter of each correct answer.

7. A structure or behavior that enables a plant to survive in its environment is its _____.

   a. habitat destruction   **b.** extinction   **c.** adaptation   **d.** propagation

8. Which of these types of plants does not reproduce by seeds?

   a. monocots   **b.** dicots   **c.** conifers   **d.** ferns

9. A plant that reproduces by cones is a _____.

   a. moss   **b.** fern   **c.** conifer   **d.** monocot

10. Liverworts, mosses, and ferns are examples of _____.

   a. nonseed plants   **b.** seed plants   **c.** dicots   **d.** monocots

Name _____ Date _____

IT'S A PLANT'S LIFE!

How much of an expert have you become on plants?
For this task, your teacher will give you and your
partner either a live or dried plant. Your job will
be to make a profile of this plant's life.

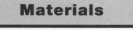

Materials

Some of these will be at your station.
- ✔ plant sample
- ✔ test tubes with stoppers
- ✔ BTB solution
- ✔ straws
- ✔ iodine solution
- ✔ medicine dropper
- ✔ graph paper
- ✔ goggles

Procedure

Safety Wear goggles during this activity. Clean up any spills
immediately. Your teacher will prepare the materials for the
iodine test. Wash your hands with soap and water when you
have finished the activity.

1. With your partner, make a list of three important characteristics of your plant. Describe the type of leaves, stems, and
roots it has. Classify the plant into the group to which you
think it belongs. Make a list of five plant processes you have
learned about in this unit. Write your list in the data space.
Decide on a plant process that you can demonstrate with the
materials you have at your station.

Name _____ Date _____

2. Look at the Task List with your partner. Decide which of you will do each task. On the line below, list the task you've chosen. In the Data Space, record your data. If you choose *Give a Demonstration*, you will be in charge of setting up the materials at your station for a demonstration of the plant process you have chosen. You should be able to explain each step of the process. If you choose *Be an Artist*, you will draw a diagram of the demonstration set-up, make a drawing of the plant parts, and graph any data that can be shown on a graph.

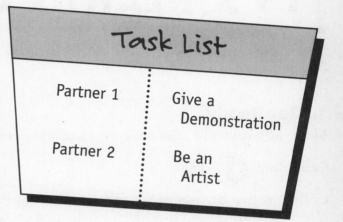

Task _____

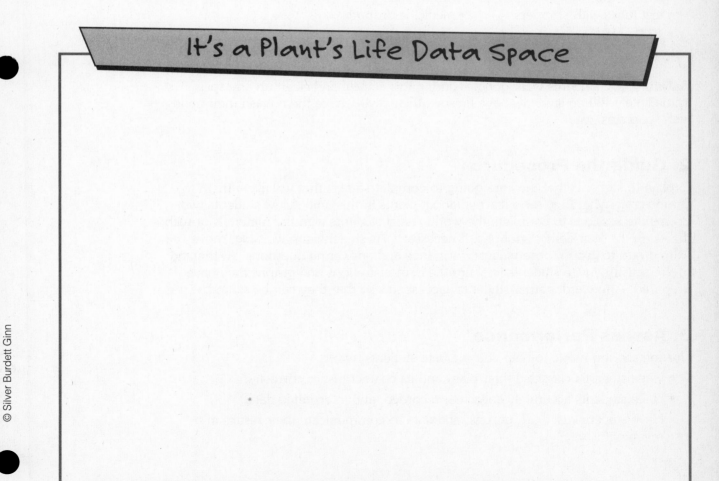

It's a Plant's Life Data Space

IT'S A PLANT'S LIFE!

Students classify a plant by its structure and choose a plant process to demonstrate.

1. Get Ready

Time: 50 minutes [2 class sessions, 25 minutes each]

Grouping: Pairs

Collaborative Strategy: You may wish to suggest that students work in groups of four, with two students working together on each task. To assess cooperative learning skills, use the Group Skills Checklist provided in this book.

Materials: (Note: Each station could have some or all of these materials depending on the availability of live or dried specimens.)

- plant sample
- test tubes with stoppers
- BTB solution
- straws
- iodine solution
- medicine dropper
- graph paper
- goggles

Safety Have students wear goggles during this activity and clean up any spills immediately. When students have finished the activity, have them wash their hands with soap and water.

2. Guide the Procedure

Explain to students that they are going to complete a task that will allow them to demonstrate what they have learned about plants in this unit. Allow students two 25-minute sessions to complete the work. Assist students with the materials or with the set-up of their demonstrations, if necessary. As students are working, move from group to group, observing performance and answering questions. At the end of the activity, invite students to share the demonstrations and graphs they have prepared. Afterward, gather students' worksheets so that they can be scored.

3. Assess Performance

Use the scoring rubric to help you evaluate students' work.
- Have students classified their plant and its characteristics correctly?
- Have students accurately collected, recorded, and interpreted data?
- Have students used art, graphs, and data to communicate their results in a meaningful way?

Name _____ Date _____

IT'S A PLANT'S LIFE!
....

Concept: Plants have structures and characteristics that enable them to carry on certain life processes.

Assessed items	Points	What to look for
Choice of Plant Process and Description	3	Student has classified and described a plant clearly and chosen a process to demonstrate.
	2	Classification, description, and plant process are indicated but are not correctly identified.
	1	Classification, description, and process are unclear or missing.
Task 1: Give a Demonstration	3	The student sets up and presents an original demonstration.
	2	The student sets up and presents a demonstration, but the material does not accurately reflect unit concepts.
	1	The work of the student is unclear or incomplete.
Task 2: Be an Artist	3	The work of the student clearly communicates the demonstration's purpose and outcome in a unique or original way.
	2	The work of the student does not accurately communicate the purpose and outcome of the demonstration.
	1	The work of the student is unclear or incomplete.
Presentation	3	Student shows good preparedness by communicating results in a meaningful way through oral presentation.
	2	Student's responses are adequate for oral presentation.
	1	Student's responses show that he or she is unprepared for oral presentation.

Name _____ Date _____

Analyze Information

For questions 1–8, circle the letter of the correct answer.

1. Why do scientists use tissue culture to produce drugs?

   a. It is expensive.

   b. It is a method of sexual reproduction.

   c. It is a method of asexual reproduction.

   d. It produces many identical, healthy plants in a short time.

2. Which of the following stages occurs first in the development of a tree?

   a. development of first leaves

   b. seed germination

   c. maturity

   d. sapling

3. The seed of a milkweed plant has a tiny parachute. How are its seeds dispersed?

   a. by bees　　**b.** by wind　　**c.** by water　　**d.** by birds

4. This low-growing plant grows only two centimeters off the ground. It is found only on the treeless plains at the very tip of South America. To which conditions has this plant become adapted?

   a. harsh wind and cold temperatures

   b. warm, tropical breezes

   c. tropical rain forest humidity

   d. warm, humid air

© Silver Burdett Ginn

Name _____ Date _____

5. A commercial flower grower wants to have plants that look exactly alike. The best way for the grower to reproduce the plants is to _____.

   a. have insects cross-pollinate the flowers

   b. have birds pollinate them

   c. do vegetative propagation

   d. have wind carry the pollen to the flowers

6. In one season, an average field of corn takes in about 5 million liters of water and gives off about 4.5 million liters of water. How does all that water leave the plants?

   a. It is released by stomata during photosynthesis.

   b. It is released by stomata during transpiration.

   c. It is combined with glucose.

   d. It evaporates from the roots.

7. In some coral reefs in the Pacific Ocean, the crown of thorns starfish feeds on the tiny animals that live inside the coral. This eventually kills the coral and has had a harmful effect on the ocean environment. This starfish gets its energy during _____.

   a. respiration

   b. photosynthesis

   c. transpiration

   d. germination

8. In a food chain, the organisms on which all else depends are the _____.

   a. decomposers

   b. first-order consumers

   c. producers

   d. second-order consumers

Name _____ Date _____

Problem Solving

9. Describe three things you used today that came from plants.

_____

_____

10. While hiking you see a hairy-cap moss that your guide book calls *Polytrichum commune*. As you travel up the mountain, you no longer see that species. Instead you see a related moss species called *Polytrichum juniperinum*. What is the probable reason for this change?

_____

_____

11. Native Americans of the Northeast used bark from birch trees to make canoes. What is bark, and why would it be a good material for this purpose?

_____

_____

12. In some places in the United States, people are experimenting with naturalizing their lawn, or letting the native plants take over. What are the advantages or disadvantages in doing this?

_____

_____

_____

_____

Name _____ Date _____

13. Look at the sketch of a cross section of a tree. Label the
heartwood. Is the tree's approximate age nearer to your age,
your parents' age, or the age your great-great grandparents
would be today? How can you tell?

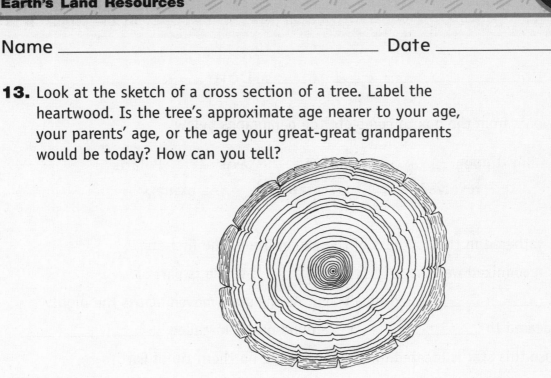

_____

_____

_____

14. Some beekeepers rent out their bees to people who own
fruit orchards. Explain why.

_____

_____

_____

Word Power

Match each term with its definition.

15. hydrotropism   a living thing that eats an herbivore

16. fruit   ground that is frozen all year long

17. xylem   structure that holds seeds

18. permafrost   asexual reproduction from part of a plant

19. vegetative propagation   water-conducting cells

20. second-order consumer   roots' growth toward water

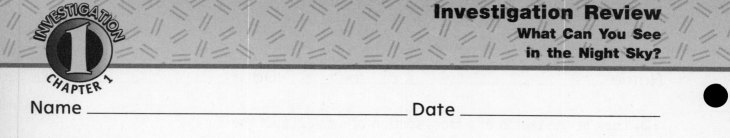
Name _____ Date _____

1. Use the words from the box to complete the paragraphs below.

Big Dipper	**constellation**	**axis**	**Polaris**
revolved	**rotate**		**planets**

Students gathered in the darkness of the planetarium. The first star

pattern they recognized was the _____, which is part of

a large _____ called Ursa Major. As the stars moved across the night

sky, they appeared to _____ around one star, called _____.

This is because this star is located directly above the northern tip of Earth's

_____. Special effects in the planetarium allowed the

students to see how different constellations looked during each season as Earth

_____ around the Sun. They also saw how _____, called

"wandering stars" by the ancient Greeks, moved across the sky.

a. What causes different stars to appear in the sky at different times of the year?

_____

b. What makes the stars appear to move from east to west across the night sky?

_____

Process Skills
Making Models, Interpreting Data

Explain how you could use a planisphere to demonstrate how the Big
Dipper can sometimes appear upside down.

_____

_____

_____

_____

Name _____ Date _____

1. Use the words in the box to answer each riddle.

comet	refracting telescope	meteorite
meteor	reflecting telescope	

a. I am made of ice, rock and debris and sometimes I'm called a dirty snowball. _____

b. Some call me a shooting star, but I am really space debris that gets burned when I enter Earth's atmosphere. _____

c. I use lenses to focus light from distant objects. _____

d. I use mirrors to gather light from distant objects. _____

e. I am all that survives of a meteor that makes it all the way to Earth's surface.

_____

2. For each telescope:
- draw an X to show where light enters the telescope;

- draw an eye to show where you would look in the telescope.

- label the type of telescope shown in each drawing.

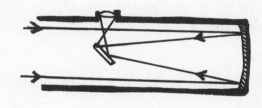

_____

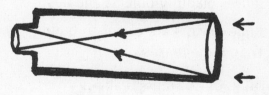

_____

Process Skills
Classifying, Inferring

Sequence these astronomer's tools from the oldest to the most recent: Hubble Space Telescope, Newton's telescope, Galileo's "ladder."

_____

CHAPTER 1

Name _____ Date _____

Analyze Information

For items 1–4, circle the letter of the correct answer.

Kurt set up a camera to take a photograph of the sky all night long. He got a picture similar to the one shown here.

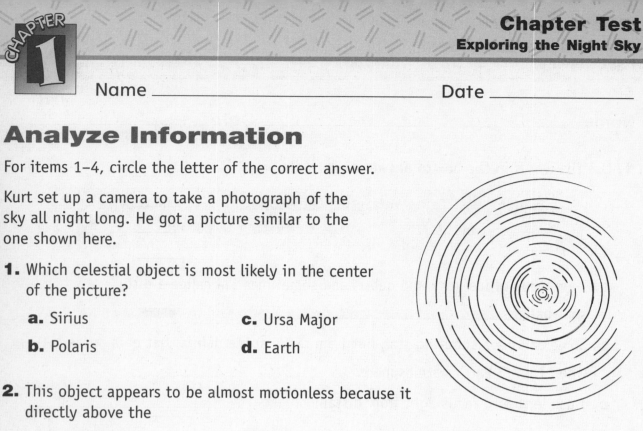

1. Which celestial object is most likely in the center of the picture?

   a. Sirius

   b. Polaris

   c. Ursa Major

   d. Earth

2. This object appears to be almost motionless because it directly above the

   a. South Pole

   b. equator

   c. Sun

   d. North Pole

3. Dust particles that speed into Earth's atmosphere and burn up are

   a. stars

   b. meteorites

   c. meteors

   d. comets

4. The largest telescopes in the world are reflecting telescopes because

   a. lenses magnify objects the best

   b. large mirrors are easier to build than large lenses

   c. mirrors are difficult to support

   d. scientists prefer reflecting telescopes

Problem Solving

5. Bob lives on the West Coast and Paige lives on the East Coast. The first person to see Venus, the evening "star," in the western sky tonight will call the other. Who will make the call? Why?

_____

_____

_____

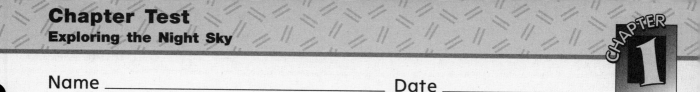

Name _____ Date _____

6. Beth, who lives in the Northern Hemisphere, loves to observe the stars. Look at Beth's constellation chart. Then answer the question.

Season	Constellations
Spring	Leo (the Lion), Bootes (the Herdsman)
Summer	Cygnus (the Swan), Lyra (the Lyre)
Autumn	Cassiopeia (the Queen), Sagittarius (the Archer)
Winter	Orion (the Hunter), Taurus (the Bull)

Why is Beth unable to see Orion in summer?

_____

_____

_____

_____

_____

_____

Word Power

Draw a line to match each word with its definition.

7. constellation   **a.** Earth's yearly trip around the Sun

8. meteorite   **b.** the spinning of Earth on its axis

9. rotation   **c.** a group of stars that forms a pattern in the night sky

10. revolution   **d.** a meteor that falls to Earth

Name _____ Date _____

1. Complete the sentences using the terms in the box.

trajectory	solar system	heliocentric model
geocentric model		Big Bang Theory

a. The idea that all the matter in the universe was once concentrated in a dense ball that then exploded is called the _____.

b. In a _____ of the solar system, the Sun and planets move around Earth.

c. In a _____ of the solar system, Earth and the other planets revolve around the Sun.

d. A star and the objects that revolve around it is called a _____.

e. The curved course a probe takes through space is called its

_____.

2. Suppose you could travel in time and could overhear an imaginary conversation between Ptolemy and Copernicus. Imagine they are discussing their views of the universe. In the space below, draw what their models might look like.

Process Skills
Making and Using Models

On a separate sheet of paper, draw a diagram to show how Earth and Mars revolve around the Sun. Show how they look when the two planets are closest together.

Name _____ Date _____

1. Draw a line from the planet to its distinguishing features.

a. Earth   closest to Sun and has craters

b. Jupiter   only planet to support life as we know it

c. Mars   smallest planet and last to be discovered

d. Mercury   has an icy moon named Triton

e. Neptune   largest planet, has Great Red Spot

f. Pluto   atmosphere of hot, swirling clouds of carbon dioxide

g. Saturn   the red planet, planet most like Earth

h. Uranus   spins on a nearly horizontal axis

i. Venus   has thousands of rings and most satellites

2. Use the diagram to compare the inner and outer planets in terms of size, composition, how they move, and presence of rings and satellites.

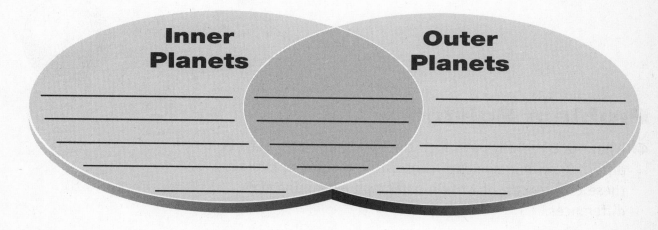

Process Skills
Communicating, Making and Using Models

On a separate sheet of paper, draw three circles to show how Earth compares with Mercury and Jupiter.

CHAPTER 2

Name _____ Date _____

Analyze Information

For items 1–3, circle the letter of the correct answer.

1. Which of the following planets is the farthest from the Sun?

   a. Jupiter   **b.** Saturn   **c.** Uranus   **d.** Neptune

2. Which of the following planets is cratered like Earth's moon?

   a. Mercury   **b.** Venus   **c.** Jupiter   **d.** Mars

3. If these objects are drawn to scale, which of the following planet-satellite pairs would they best represent?

   a. Jupiter and Io

   b. Mars and Phobos

   c. Saturn and Titan

   d. Pluto and Charon

Problem Solving

4. What are three ways in which the inner and outer planets differ? Draw and label two contrasting planets to explain these differences, or write a paragraph explaining the differences.

Name _____ Date _____

5. Explain the different views of the solar system
of Ptolemy and Copernicus.

_____

_____

_____

_____

_____

_____

Word Power

Use the words in the box to complete the paragraph below.

Jupiter	Neptune	Saturn	Uranus

   In 1977, two *Voyager* space probes were sent on trajectories that would take
them millions of kilometers to four of the outer planets. When they passed by the
closest giant planet, _____, they took pictures of its Great Red Spot
and its thin ring that can't be seen from Earth. Because of the way the orbits of
the planets lined up, the space probes used gravity assist to get them on a path
to the next planet, _____. Dazzling photographs showed that its
famous rings were made of rocks and ice of different sizes and colors. *Voyager 2*
then went to blue-green _____. Pictures taken there showed that its
axis is tilted over on its side. The last planet photographed, _____,
has swirling, bluish features that are similar to those of Jupiter and Saturn.

Name _____ Date _____

1. Underline the correct answer within the parentheses.

  a. The temperature and (size, distance, color) of a star are closely linked.

  b. Stars with the coolest temperatures shine with a (bluish, white, red) light.

  c. The energy of a star is generated in the (center, surface, edges) of the star.

  d. Stars produce energy by converting (carbon, hydrogen, gravity) to helium.

2. Match star color and approximate surface temperature.

Color	Surface Temperature
Yellow	6,000°–7,500°C
Blue	7,500°–11,000°C
Red	5,000°–6,000°C
White	11,000°–50,000°C
Blue-white	2,000°–3,500°C

Process Skills
Experimenting

Suppose you have a friend who does not believe that white light contains many different colors. Using materials from the activity "Capturing Colors," what could you do to show your friend the colors of the spectrum?

_____

_____

_____

_____

_____

© Silver Burdett Ginn

Name _____ Date _____

1. Circle the letter of the correct answer.

A. What unit would an astronomer likely use in describing the distance to a star?

a. kilometers   **b.** meters   **c.** astronomical units   **d.** light years

B. A bright star can appear dimmer than a less bright star if the bright star is _____.

a. farther away   **b.** closer   **c.** bluish   **d.** cool

2. Look at the diagram. Describe the method being used to find the distance to star X.

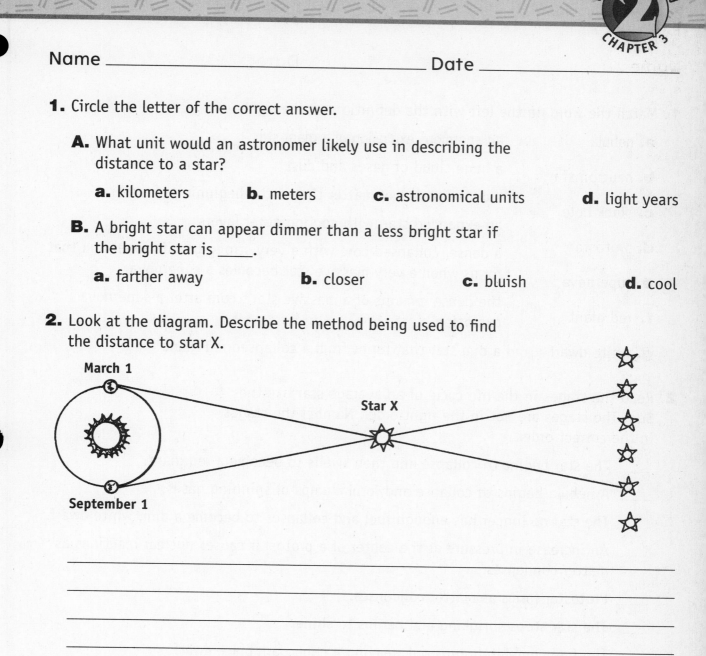

March 1

September 1

Star X

_____

_____

_____

_____

Process Skills
Comparing/Contrasting

Compare and contrast apparent magnitude and absolute magnitude.

_____

_____

_____

Name _____ Date _____

1. Match the word on the left with the definition on the right.

a. nebula   an enormous explosion of a giant star

b. neutron star   a huge cloud of gases and dust

c. black hole   a dense pocket of matter that is the beginning of a star

                       an expanded star, with cooling outer layers

d. protostar   a dense, collapsed core with a very strong gravitational pull that
e. supernova   forms when a very massive star becomes a supernova

                       the dense remains of a massive star's core after a supernova
f. red giant   explosion

g. white dwarf   a dim star that forms from a collapsed red giant

2. Read the stages in the life cycle of an average star like the
Sun. The stages are not in the right order. Number the stages
in the correct order.

_____ The star begins to collapse and then swells to become a red giant.

_____ A nebula begins to collapse and form clumps of spinning gases.

_____ The star no longer has enough fuel and collapses to become a dim, white dwarf.

_____ An increase in pressure at the center of a protostar causes nuclear reactions as
matter condenses.

_____ Protostar forms as matter condenses.

_____ The star stops shrinking and begins to shine.

_____ The fuel completely runs out, leaving a cool, dark black dwarf

Process Skills
Hypothesizing

In 1993, an amateur astronomer discovered a bright object in a
nearby galaxy. It was larger and brighter than our Sun. Its
spectrum showed that most of its hydrogen was gone. Based on
these observations, what could you hypothesize the object was?

_____

_____

Investigation Review
What Are Galaxies and How Do They Differ?

Name _____ Date _____

1. Use the words from the box to complete the paragraph below.

elliptical	**galaxies**	**irregular**
spiral	**stars**	

There may be as many as 100 billion _____ in the universe, each containing billions of _____. The most common type of galaxy is _____. Our galaxy has spreading arms and a _____ shape. Galaxies with no definite shape are classified as _____.

2. Imagine that you have made the batter for a raisin cake. As the cake bakes, the batter rises and the cake gets larger. Suppose the raisins represent galaxies. Use this analogy to explain what is happening to the galaxies of the universe.

_____

_____

_____

_____

Process Skills
Classifying

What kind of galaxy is shown in the picture? How does it compare to our own?

_____

_____

_____

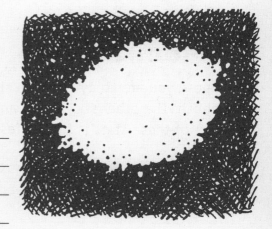

CHAPTER 3

Name _____ Date _____

Analyze Information

For items 1–3, circle the letter of the correct answer.

1. Suppose you are collecting data about a new star. Which of the following is *least* likely to be one of its features?

a. It has a yellow color.

b. It is an average-sized star.

c. It has a surface temperature of 6,000°C.

d. It is 100,000 light-years across.

2. The gas that fuels the "furnaces" of stars for most of their "lives" is ____.

a. hydrogen   **b.** helium   **c.** oxygen   **d.** plasma

3. Astronomers looking at the light coming from a star hypothesize that it is a red giant. Which of the following shows the order of the probable stages in the life of that star to this point?

a. white dwarf, black hole, neutron star, red giant

b. nebula, shining star, white dwarf, red giant

c. shining star, protostar, supernova, red giant

d. nebula, protostar, shining star, red giant

Problem Solving

4. Suppose you are studying three stars. You know that one star is bluish, the other star is red, and the third star is white. Which of these stars is the hottest? The coolest? Explain.

_____

_____

_____

Name _____ Date _____

5. You have been hired by NASA to make a package of present-day items that will travel in a space vehicle to another galaxy. In the space provided, draw or write "Earth's galaxy address" on the package so it can be returned to Earth if lost.

6. An astronomer is studying a bright star in the night sky. How can the astronomer determine how bright the star really is, if it is relatively close to Earth?

_____

_____

_____

_____

Word Power

7. The (galaxy, universe) is made up of absolutely everything that exists.

8. A very massive star might end its life as a (black hole, black dwarf).

9. The (apparent, absolute) magnitude of a star is its actual brightness.

10. Everything in the universe is moving (away from, towards) each other.

INVESTIGATION 1
CHAPTER 4

Name _____ Date _____

1. What is free fall and when are astronauts in free fall? What does free fall have to do with weightlessness?

_____

_____

_____

2. Suppose you are a medical officer on a space shuttle. You know that certain changes in the human body are normal and expected in space. Complete the checklist below of changes to look for during your space mission.

Medical Checklist		
Types of changes	**Examples**	**Reasons**
Changes in height		
Changes in the heart		
Changes in fluid balance		

Process Skills
Inferring

Choose one part of your daily routine and imagine how you would accomplish that routine on board a space shuttle. Write your answer on a separate sheet of paper.

Name _____ Date _____

1. Label the arrows to show the exchange of oxygen and carbon
dioxide between organisms.

2. Underline the correct answer within the parentheses.

a. The (biosphere, water cycle) is a natural system that provides
living things with all their needs.

b. When people breathe, they take in (oxygen, carbon dioxide)
and release (oxygen, carbon dioxide).

Process Skills
Concluding, Inferring

When astronauts go out of the shuttle to do repairs, they wear a portable
life-support system. List two things provided by this important piece of
equipment and explain why each is necessary.

_____

_____

_____

_____

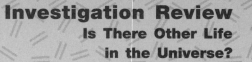

INVESTIGATION 3
CHAPTER 4

Name _____ Date _____

1. Match the word on the left with the description on the right.

a. radio telescope   a form of electromagnetic radiation

b. Voyager   anything that comes from beyond Earth

c. radio wave   the search for extraterrestrial intelligence using
                                       radio telescopes

d. extraterrestrial   giant antennas that receive radio signals

e. Drake equation   space probe carrying sound disk to tell alien people
                                       about our planet

f. SETI   way of estimating the chances of communicating
                                       with extraterrestrials

2. Explain in general terms how the Drake equation estimates the
odds of communicating with extraterrestrial life.

_____

_____

_____

_____

_____

Process Skills
Communicating

Write a message about an important aspect of life on Earth to be
sent beyond our solar system.

_____

_____

_____

Name _____ Date _____

Analyze Information

For questions 1–2, circle the letter of the correct answer.

1. Astronauts who spend time on board a space shuttle experience several changes in their bodies. Which is the <u>least</u> likely to happen?

    a. a plugged-up nose

    b. a slight gain in height

    c. gain of muscle strength

    d. a slight loss of calcium

2. Which of the following is not one of the factors in the Drake equation?

    a. the ability to use sound to communicate

    b. the average life span of a civilization

    c. the number of habitable planets

    d. the number of planets that develop intelligent life

Problem Solving

3. Suppose you are going to be in space for a very long time. Explain how you would provide and conserve oxygen on the trip.

_____

_____

_____

_____

4. Each year students at Space Camp in Huntsville, Alabama, learn what it's like to be an astronaut in space. Suppose you were in charge of a space camp. List at least two programs that you would design to provide a realistic experience of life in space.

_____

_____

_____

_____

Name _____ Date _____

5. Make a list of things to take on a trip into space. Put a star by the most important choices.

_____

_____

_____

_____

_____

6. Both you and your neighbor have lamps in your bedrooms. Suppose both lamps have timers that randomly turn the lights on for one second each day. How would you describe the conditions under which both lights would be on at the same time? Use this analogy to discuss the chances of communicating with intelligent extraterrestrial life.

_____

_____

_____

_____

_____

_____

Word Power

Match each word on the left with its description on the right.

7. free fall   a feeling, experienced in free fall, that there is no gravity

8. extraterrestrial   self-contained and self-sustaining natural system

9. weightlessness   condition in which there is no resistance to the pull of gravity

10. biosphere   anything that comes from beyond Earth

Name _____ Date _____

OUR PLACE IN SPACE

· ·

Our space address is pretty easy to remember: Third planet from the Sun, Solar System, Milky Way Galaxy. Suppose you and your team want to demonstrate what this means to some-one who has never studied the solar system. Your task will be to create a simple model to show where we are in space.

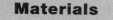

Materials

✔ crayons or markers
✔ several balls of different sizes
✔ text or reference books of constellation patterns

Procedure

1. You and your team will create a model of part of our solar system. As a team, choose two other planets besides Earth that you would like to include in your model. Also, choose one constellation that you wish to represent. On the lines below, list the planets and the constellation that you've chosen. Include the most distinguishing features about each.

_____

_____

_____

_____

_____

Name _____ Date _____

2. Look at the Task List with your partners. Decide which of you will do each
task. On the line below, list the task
you've chosen. If you choose *Gather the
Planets and Sun,* find several balls that
best represent the planets you will
model, based on their relative sizes. If
you choose *Where in Relation to Sun,* determine where each planet in your model
should be in relation to the Sun. If you
choose *Show the Stars*, make a sketch of the constellation
that your group has chosen. When you have completed your
task, work together to draw a diagram in the Data Space to
show how you would arrange these materials to make a
useful model. Show how the planets, the Sun, and the constellation
would have to be positioned in order to be visible from Earth.

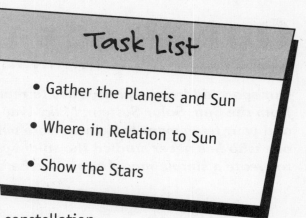

Task _____

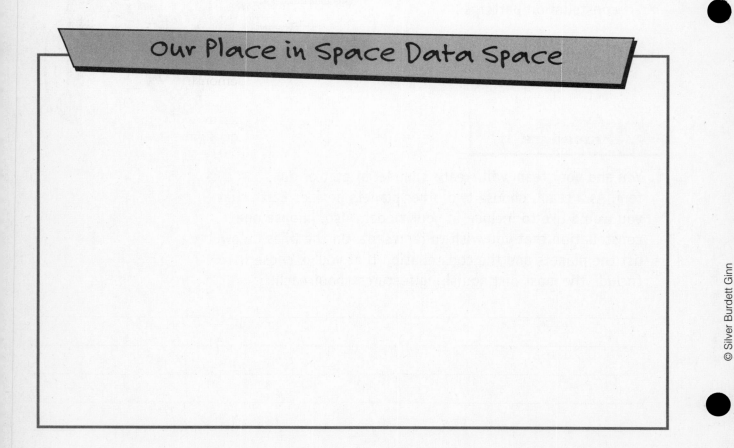

OUR PLACE IN SPACE

Students make a model that shows our space address using balls to represent planets and the Sun. Students should demonstrate an understanding of the relative positions of each celestial body in order for each to be visible from Earth.

1. Get Ready

Time: 50 minutes

Grouping: Small Groups

Collaborative Strategy: You may wish to suggest that students work in groups of six, with two students working on each task. To assess cooperative learning skills, use the Group Skills Checklist provided in this book.

Materials: (each station)
- crayons or markers
- assorted balls for students to choose as models
- text or reference books for constellation patterns

2. Guide the Procedure

Place the materials needed for the tasks at each station and identify student teams. Explain to students that they are going to make a model of part of the solar system using balls to represent the planets and the Sun. They will also be demonstrating how a constellation must be positioned to be visible from Earth.

Allow students to complete their tasks within 30 minutes. As students are working, move from group to group, observing performance and answering questions. After students complete the data table information ask them to demonstrate how the model planets are lined up in order to be visible from Earth. Also ask students to explain the constellation's relative place in the sky for it to be visible from Earth. Allow each group several minutes to present their models to the class. Afterwards, gather students' worksheets so that they can be scored.

3. Assess the Performance

Use the scoring rubric to help you evaluate students' work.
- Have they chosen balls that accurately represent the relative sizes of the planets in their models?
- Have students effectively communicated the distances in space?
- Have they created models that represent the planets and constellations accurately?

Name _____ Date _____

OUR PLACE IN SPACE

Concept: Planets in the solar system and constellations within the galaxy are visible from Earth depending on their position in the sky.

Assessed items	Points	What to look for
Planet and Constellation Features	3	Planet data includes: relative size, composition, distinguishing features, and relative distance from the Sun; constellation data includes a description of the group of stars and when visible.
	2	Some of the data is inaccurate.
	1	Data is unclear, missing, or entirely inaccurate.
Task: Gather the Planets	3	The several balls chosen for the model clearly represent the relative sizes of the planets.
	2	One ball chosen does not clearly represent the relative size of a planet.
	1	Two or more balls chosen do not clearly represent the sizes of planets.
Task: How Far From Earth	3	The approximate distances to all planets from the Sun in the model are calculated accurately.
	2	The approximate distance for one planet is inaccurate.
	1	The approximate distances for both planets are inaccurate.
Task: Show the Stars	3	The sketch accurately represents the constellation.
	2	The sketch only partly represents the constellation.
	1	The sketch inaccurately represents the constellation.
Draw the Model	3	The diagram accurately shows the relative positions of the planets and constellation, as seen from Earth.
	2	The diagram accurately places the orbits of the planets, but fails to show when a celestial object is visible from Earth.
	1	The diagram is unclear, inaccurate, or incomplete.

Name _____ Date _____

Analyze Information

1. Look at the picture of a comet in its orbit around the Sun. Draw a tail on the comet in each position as it goes around the Sun.

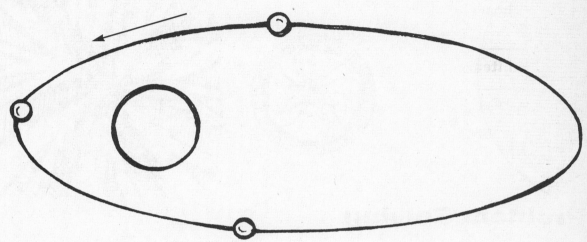

For items 2–3, circle the letter of the correct answer.

2. The largest telescopes are reflectors because

   a. lenses are easier to make

   b. mirrors break easily

   c. large mirrors can be completely supported

   d. large lenses are lighter than mirrors

3. The Hubble Telescope can see more clearly than many of the telescopes on the ground because _____.

   a. it has a higher power than any of them

   b. it is a refracting telescope

   c. it is positioned beyond our planet's atmosphere

   d. it moves quickly in space

4. Write the three most important things you would need to include in a life-support system to use in space.

_____

© Silver Burdett Ginn

Name _____ Date _____

5. Using the terms *supernova*, *collapsed star*, and *massive star*, identify the three stages diagramed below.

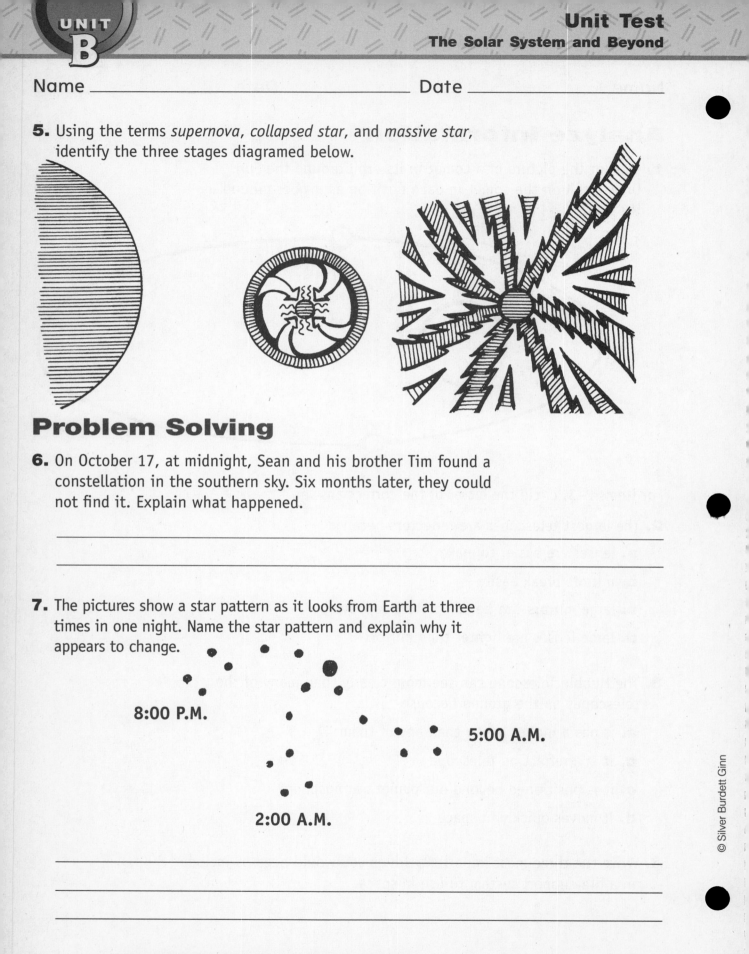

Problem Solving

6. On October 17, at midnight, Sean and his brother Tim found a constellation in the southern sky. Six months later, they could not find it. Explain what happened.

_____

_____

7. The pictures show a star pattern as it looks from Earth at three times in one night. Name the star pattern and explain why it appears to change.

8:00 P.M.

2:00 A.M.

5:00 A.M.

_____

_____

_____

Name _____ Date _____

8. Choose an inner planet and an outer planet and tell how they differ.

_____

_____

_____

_____

_____

9. Would you classify Pluto as an inner or outer planet? Explain your answer.

_____

_____

_____

_____

10. You are asked to write the in-flight instructions for the people who will take a space shuttle into space. What should you tell them about the effects of weightlessness on the human body and how they can adjust to these changes?

_____

_____

_____

Word Power

Circle the letter of the answer that best completes each sentence.

11. When you are temporarily "weightless" at the top of a swing on the playground, you are in _____.

a. free fall   **b.** microgravity   **c.** space   **d.** revolution

Name _____ Date _____

12. A meteorite is an example of a(n) ____.

    a. planet   **b.** comet   **c.** space probe   **d.** extraterrestrial object

13. An uncrewed space probe would probably not have a ____.

    a. biosphere   **b.** telescope   **c.** camera   **d.** rocket

14. The inner planets are also called ____.

    a. "sister" planets   **b.** gas giants   **c.** terrestrial planets   **d.** extraterrestrial planets

15. ____ are bits of dust and rock that reach Earth's surface and that help astronomers learn about the origins of the solar system.

    a. Comets   **b.** Meteors   **c.** Constellations   **d.** Meteorites

16. A unit that is commonly used to measure distances in space is the ____.

    a. newton   **b.** meter   **c.** light year   **d.** yard

17. Measuring ____ is the most helpful method of calculating distances to nearby stars.

    a. size   **b.** magnitude   **c.** color   **d.** parallax

18. A star probably begins as a cloud of gases and dust in space known as a ____.

    a. nebula   **b.** comet   **c.** constellation   **d.** planet

19. Two stars revolving around the same point make up a system called a ____.

    a. dwarf   **b.** black hole   **c.** binary star   **d.** white star

20. The pockets of dense matter that form the beginning of stars are ____.

    a. comets   **b.** protostars   **c.** dwarfs   **d.** neutrons

© Silver Burdett Ginn

Name _____ Date _____

1. Look at the drawing. Label the types of energy you see. Use these terms: mechanical, stored, heat, radiant, electricity.

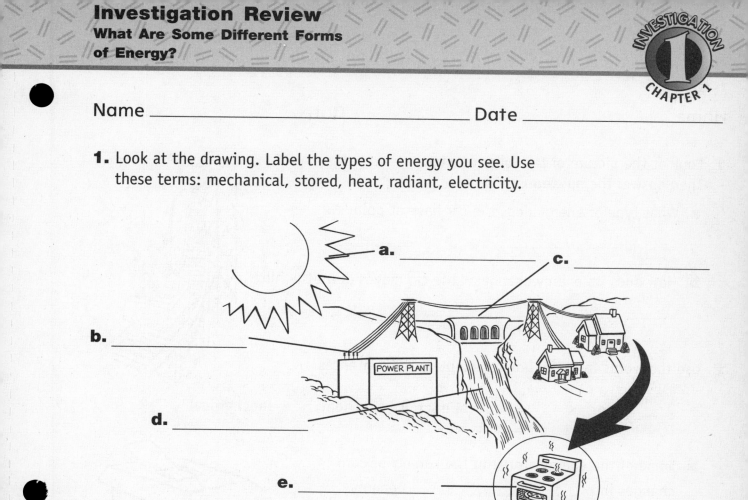

a. _____

c. _____

b. _____

d. _____

e. _____

POWER PLANT

2. Use the diagram to answer the following questions.

a. If you touched the hot pizza in the oven, how would the heat energy be transferred to your hand?

_____

b. Explain where stored energy is being changed to mechanical energy.

_____

c. What kind of energy does not need a medium through which to travel?

_____

Process Skills
Inferring

How could you use a toy glider with a wind-up propeller to demonstrate that energy can be stored in a rubber band? Write your answer on a separate sheet of paper.

© Silver Burdett Ginn

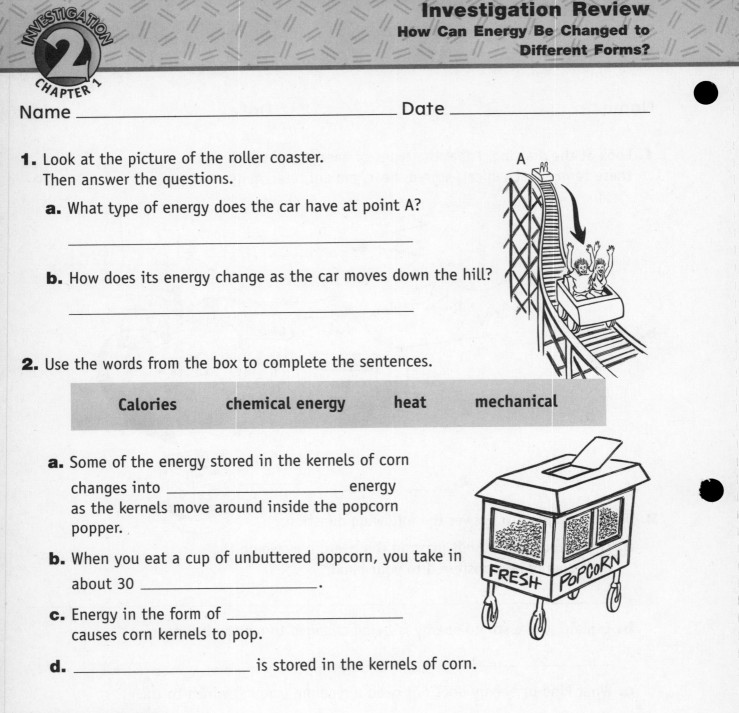

Name _____ Date _____

1. Look at the picture of the roller coaster. Then answer the questions.

  a. What type of energy does the car have at point A?

  _____

  b. How does its energy change as the car moves down the hill?

  _____

2. Use the words from the box to complete the sentences.

Calories	chemical energy	heat	mechanical

  a. Some of the energy stored in the kernels of corn changes into _____ energy as the kernels move around inside the popcorn popper.

  b. When you eat a cup of unbuttered popcorn, you take in about 30 _____.

  c. Energy in the form of _____ causes corn kernels to pop.

  d. _____ is stored in the kernels of corn.

Process Skills
Inferring, Communicating

Suppose Joan dives from a diving board. What kind of energy does she have as she stands on the board? How does her energy change when she moves off the board?

_____

_____

_____

Name _____ Date _____

1. Look at the two pictures below. Write *W* on the line below the picture that shows work being done. Write *N* below the picture showing no work being done.

_____   _____

2. Use the words from the box to complete the sentences.

Joule	less	Newton	resistance	work

a. Gravity and friction are _____ forces.

b. _____ = force × distance

c. A unit for measuring force is named in honor of Isaac _____.

d. If you move an object over a short distance, you do _____ work than if you move the same object over a long distance.

e. The _____ is a unit for measuring work.

Process Skills
Making a Hypothesis

Suppose you are watching some children on a slide in the play-ground. Some of them sit on sheets of waxed paper, and some do not. The children who don't use waxed paper go down the slide more slowly than those who do. Make a hypothesis to explain why. Write your answer on a separate sheet of paper.

Chapter **1**

Name _____ Date _____

Analyze Information

1. A baseball is on top of the refrigerator. A second baseball is on the kitchen table. Which baseball has more potential energy? Explain your answer.

_____

_____

For questions 2-3, circle the correct answer.

2. When Sandra added some oil to her skateboard wheels, she found that she could glide farther and faster. Why?

   a. rolling friction is less than sliding friction

   b. she used a fluid lubricant

   c. she was changing more potential energy into kinetic energy

   d. she increased the amount of sliding friction

3. Suppose you were at the blastoff of a space shuttle. What are some forms of energy you could observe?

   a. heat

   b. light and sound

   c. mechanical

   d. all of the above

4. What forces are resisting the efforts of each person in the picture?

_____

_____

_____

_____

_____

© Silver Burdett Ginn

Name _____ Date _____

Problem Solving

5. Who is doing more work in the picture? Explain your answer.

_____

_____

6. Suppose you step into an elevator on the 80th floor of a sky-scraper. You are munching a granola bar as you press the button for the ground floor. Describe the stored energy around you and how it will change.

_____

_____

_____

_____

Word Power

Fill in the concept map. Use the words from the box.

joules	kinetic energy	potential energy	work

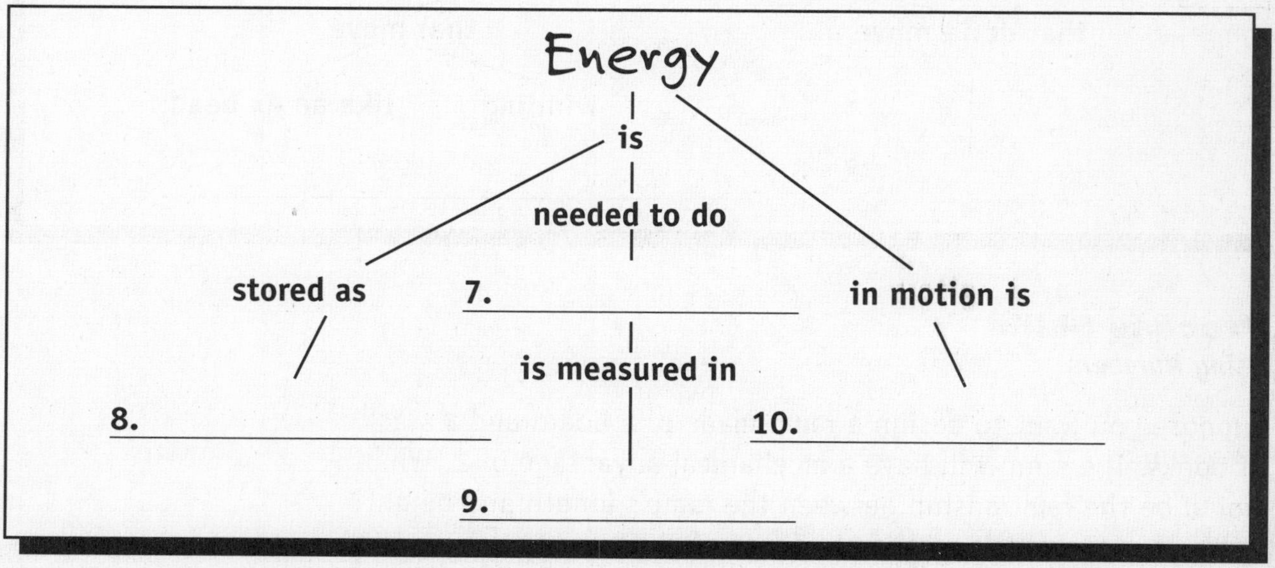

Energy

is

needed to do

stored as   7. _____   in motion is

is measured in

8. _____   10. _____

9. _____

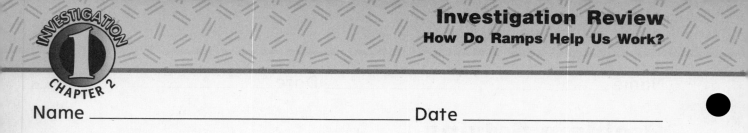
Name _____ Date _____

1. Fill in the blanks on and below the pictures. Use the words in the box.

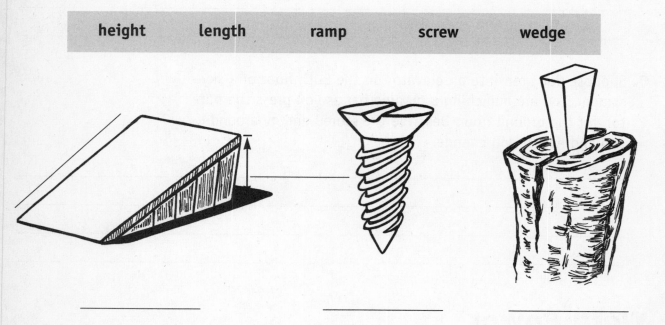

| height | length | ramp | screw | wedge |

_____   _____   _____

2. Complete the concept map below about inclined planes.

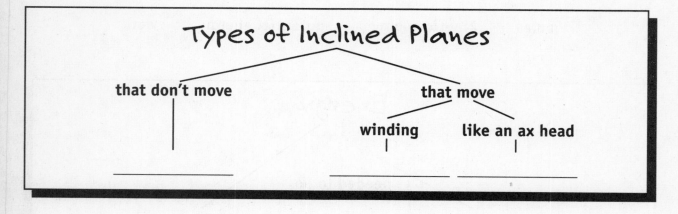

Types of Inclined Planes

that don't move   that move

_____   winding   like an ax head

_____   _____   _____

Process Skills
Using Numbers

Suppose you want to design a ramp made of a board and a stack of books. The ramp will have a mechanical advantage of 2. What would be the relationship between the ramp's length and height? Write your answer on a separate sheet of paper.

Name _____ Date _____

1. Look at the pictures of the three classes of levers. Label the fulcrum, show with arrows where you apply the effort force, and write a 1, 2, or 3 to identify the first, second, and third class lever.

2. On the line under each drawing, write the name of the type of pulley shown. Then explain which type of pulley you would use to raise a flag to the top of a flagpole.

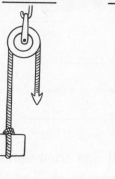

_____   _____
_____   _____

_____
_____
_____

Process Skills
Inferring

Two friends are on a seesaw. They can balance the seesaw if Mike sits near the end and Terry sits close to the middle. What can you infer about the relative masses of the two friends?

_____

INVESTIGATION **3** CHAPTER 2

Name _____ Date _____

1. **a.** On the lines provided, name the parts of the windmill. Use the terms in the word box.

   chain
   windmill blades
   generator
   gears
   windmill shaft
   generator shaft

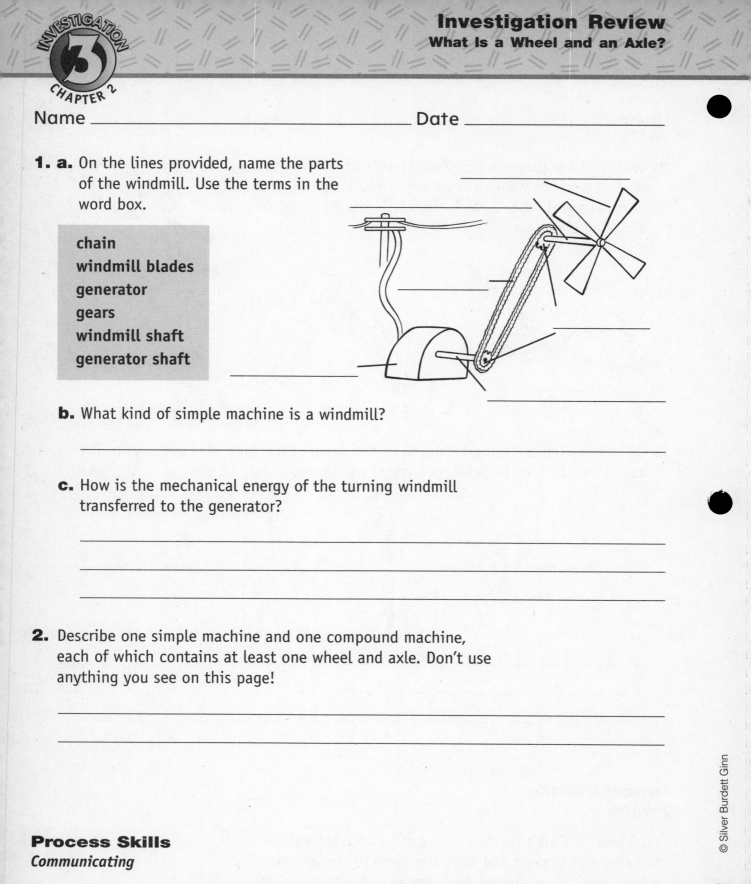

   b. What kind of simple machine is a windmill?

   _____

   c. How is the mechanical energy of the turning windmill transferred to the generator?

   _____

   _____

   _____

2. Describe one simple machine and one compound machine, each of which contains at least one wheel and axle. Don't use anything you see on this page!

   _____

   _____

Process Skills
Communicating

On a separate sheet of paper explain how an airplane propeller is similar to a Ferris wheel.

Name _____ Date _____

Analyze Information

1. What can the person do to make
   this job easier? Explain.

   _____

   _____

.5 m

2. What will happen to the amount of
   work done if the job is made easier?

   _____

3. Label the wheel and axle at the back of the bike.
   Also, label the gears.

   _____

   _____

   _____

4. What type of machine is a hand brake? _____
   Draw an arrow on the bike above to show where effort is applied.

Problem Solving

5. What is the advantage of using a compound machine over
   using a simple machine?

   _____

   _____

Name _____ Date _____

6. Look at the drawing of a mechanic using a compound machine to move a car from the ground up onto a flatbed truck. On each line, write the name of the simple machine that is a part of the compound machine.

Word Power

Circle the letter of the correct answer.

7. A wheelbarrow, a car jack, and a crowbar are all examples of _____ .

a. levers   **b.** pulleys   **c.** ramps   **d.** wheel and axles

8. A screw is a type of _____ that moves and can be used to raise or lower something.

a. wedge   **b.** pulley   **c.** inclined plane   **d.** lever

9. A wrench is an example of a(n)_____.

a. inclined plane   **b.** pulley   **c.** wheel and axle   **d.** gear

10. If you want to change the direction of your effort force without multiplying that force, which would you use?

a. pulley   **c.** wheel and axle

b. third-class lever   **d.** second-class lever

Name _____ Date _____

GO ON A
SCAVENGER HUNT
....

You and your partners are going on a different kind of scavenger hunt. You'll be looking for simple machines and energy "changers" that are "hidden" in everyday things. First, prepare a list of things to look for. Then, swap lists with another group and look for the things on their list.

Procedure

1. Make a list of things to look for on the scavenger hunt. For ideas, look through photographs and drawings of machines and energy changers from your textbook, reference books, or from objects in your classroom or school. You need to come up with two different simple machines and two other devices that change energy from one kind to another. When you have finished your list, your teacher will approve it. Then you will get a copy of another group's list. The hunt is on!

> ### Task List
>
> Give a Talk
>
> Show How It Works
>
> Find Other Examples

2. With your new list, search through magazines for pictures or identify machines or devices within your classroom to find each kind of machine or device on the list. Write all the things you find in your Data Space on page 84.

3. Once you have completed your scavenger hunt, choose one of the tasks from the Task List.

If you choose *Give a Talk,* discuss the energy changers on your list. Identify the type of energy it uses and the energy change produced by each energy changer.

Name _____ Date _____

If you choose *Show How It Works,* show how each simple machine works by demonstrating a simple version of each machine and how friction affects its performance.

If you choose *Find Other Examples,* you should identify other machines or energy-changing devices similar to those on your list.

Scavenger Hunt Data Space

GO ON A
SCAVENGER HUNT

Students should demonstrate an understanding that many devices in everyday life change energy from one form to another or help us to do work.

1. Get Ready

Time: 60 minutes

Grouping: Small Groups

Collaborative Strategy: You may wish to have students work in groups of threes or sixes. Use the Group Skills Checklist provided in this book to assess students' cooperative learning skills.

2. Guide the Procedure

Remind students that their work will show how well they understand the ideas in this unit. As students are working, observe performance and answer questions. Afterwards, gather students' worksheets so that they can be scored.

3. Assess the Performance

Use the scoring rubric to help you evaluate students' work.

- Have students used the science concepts in the unit to make good decisions about the machines and devices?
- Have students identified the correct machines and devices from the list?
- Have students created diagrams or used actual machines and energy "changers"?
- Did they effectively show their aptitude for manipulating objects?

Name _____ Date _____

GO ON A
SCAVENGER HUNT

Concept: Many devices in everyday life change energy from one form to another or help us to do work.

Assessed items	Points	What to look for
Writing a Scavenger Hunt List	3	The machines and energy-changing devices, with familiar examples, are clearly indicated and list is complete.
	2	One machine or device is missing from the list.
	1	List of machines and devices is unclear or incomplete.
Finding the Machines and Devices	3	The machines and devices collected match those on the list, and the descriptions of what various machines and devices can do are clearly indicated.
	2	At least one machine or device from the list is missing from the collection and/or one or more descriptions is missing or inaccurate.
	1	Collection of devices and machines is incomplete or unclear.
Completing the Task	3	Chosen task is completed clearly and accurately.
	2	All parts of the chosen task are carried out to some degree.
	1	Work is unclear or incomplete.

Name _____ Date _____

Analyze Information

In the middle 1800s, James Prescott Joule made things fall, spin, and heat up in his experiments. The picture shows how he demonstrated that mechanical energy from a falling weight can be changed into heat energy. Each time Joule let a weight fall, it would cause the paddle wheel to turn under the water. The turning wheel then caused the temperature of the water in the tank to increase.

1. Suppose Joule allowed a weight of 2 N to fall through a distance of 1 meter. How much work would be done?

_____

_____

2. Describe the energy change that takes place as the weight drops.

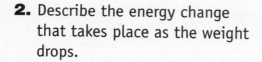

_____

_____

_____

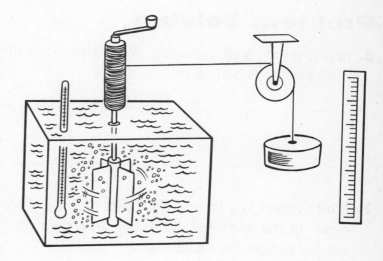

3. Suppose a 10-newton weight drops through 2 meters. Would the temperature change of the water be more or less than with the 2-N weight? Describe the energy changes that take place.

_____

_____

_____

_____

Name _____ Date _____

4. What two simple machines did Joule use to raise the weight?

_____

5. Energy can cause changes in position, direction, or temperature. Describe three ways Joule might have observed these changes.

_____

_____

_____

_____

_____

Problem Solving

6. How is energy stored in a log? What happens to this energy when the log is burned?

_____

_____

_____

7. Tabita's mass is 5 kg less than that of Sean. Who should sit closer to the middle of a seesaw? Draw their positions on the seesaw so that they balance.

8. Thousands of years ago, a king asked a Greek philosopher named Archimedes to pull a ship through the water all by himself. Archimedes met the challenge! Do you think he used a wedge, a pulley, or a lever to help him? Explain your answer.

_____

_____

Name _____ Date _____

9. How would you demonstrate stored energy in a balloon?

_____

_____

_____

10. If you hike Angel Creek Trail to reach the bottom of the Grand Canyon, you travel about 7 times farther than the Grand Canyon is deep. Make a drawing of a simple machine and use it to explain why this is so.

11. Write three sentences in which you show the relationship among energy, work, and force.

_____

_____

_____

Word Power

Circle the letter of the correct answer.

12. Chopsticks are used by some people. These eating tools are examples of _____.

    a. pulleys   **c.** inclined planes

    b. levers   **d.** wedges

13. A doorknob is an example of a(n) _____.

    a. pulley   **c.** wheel and axle

    b. inclined plane   **d.** wedge

Name _____ Date _____

14. If you exert a force over a distance, ____ is done.

    a. potential energy   **c.** friction

    b. resistance   **d.** work

15. The force you exert on a simple machine is called the ____ force.

    a. resistance   **c.** positive

    b. friction   **d.** effort

16. A push or a pull best describes ____.

    a. energy   **c.** force

    b. work   **d.** mechanical advantage

17. Something that changes the direction of a force or multiplies a force is probably a ____.

    a. simple machine   **c.** power plant

    b. third-class lever   **d.** storage battery

18. The ability to cause a change in position, direction, or temperature is ____.

    a. work   **c.** resistance

    b. energy   **d.** force

19. Which method of energy transfer does not need a medium through which to travel?

    a. radiation   **c.** convection

    b. conduction   **d.** mechanical

20. The amount of energy stored in an object is likely to be measured in ____.

    a. newtons   **c.** joules

    b. kilograms   **d.** degrees Celsius

Name _____ Date _____

1. Identify each factor below as either biotic or abiotic.

    a. ladybird beetle _____   **d.** earthworm _____

    b. snow _____   **e.** rock _____

    c. maple tree _____   **f.** mosquito _____

2. Use the terms in the box to complete the concept map below.

soil	abiotic	community	populations
temperature	biotic	rocks	species

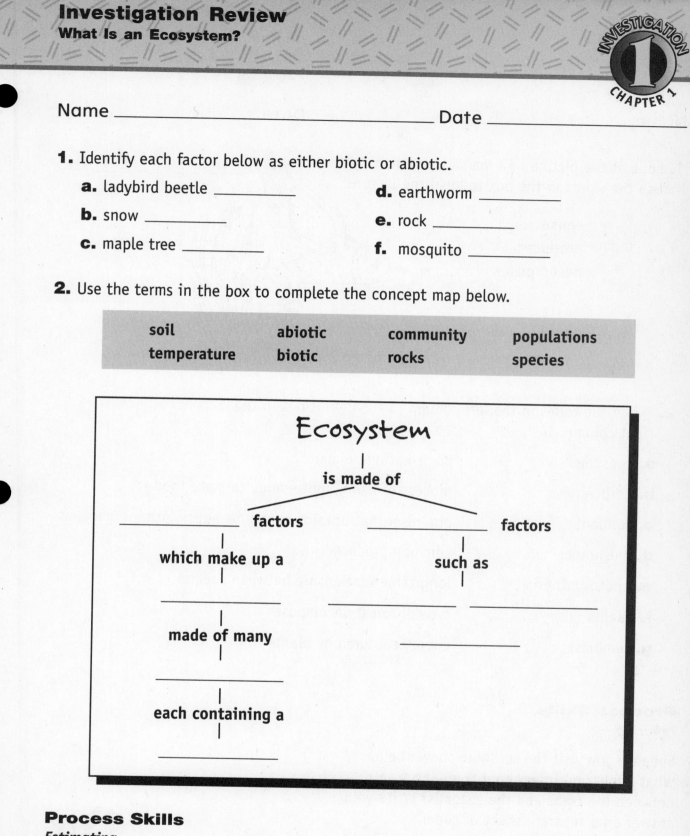

Ecosystem

is made of

_____ factors   _____ factors

which make up a   such as

_____   _____

made of many   _____

_____

each containing a

_____

Process Skills
Estimating

How could you estimate how many trees are growing in a large wooded area near where you live? Write your answer on a separate sheet of paper.

Name _____ Date _____

1. Look at the picture of a marsh ecosystem.
Use the words in the box to label the picture.

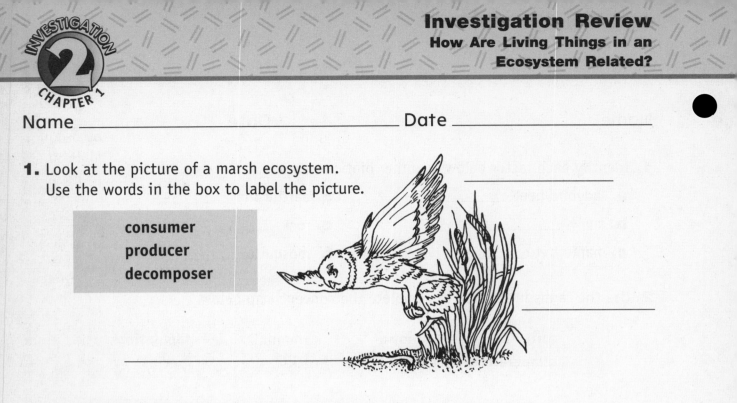

| consumer |
| producer |
| decomposer |

_____

_____

_____

2. Match the terms in the left column to the definitions in the
right column.

a. consumer   plant-eating animal

b. herbivore   process of using light energy to make food

c. sunlight   organism that obtains energy by eating other organisms

d. mushroom   common producers

e. photosynthesis   long term relationship between species

f. plants   type of forest decomposer

g. symbiosis   energy captured by plants

Process Skills

Inferring

Suppose you visit the seashore shown below.
What might you infer about the relationship
between the crabs and the seagulls? Write your
answer on a separate sheet of paper.

Name _____ Date _____

Analyze Information

1. Three of the words below are the same in some way. Which word does not belong with the others? Why?

| white-footed mouse | dragonfly | snow | maple tree |

_____

2. Reorder these terms from smallest to largest.

ecosystem   community   population

_____

3. In an African marsh, a hippopotamus munches on water cabbage. The huge animal stirs up the muddy water, helping to get plant food to snails that live in the marsh. The abundance of snails provides food for open-bill storks. Write the name of the organisms mentioned that fit each term.

a. producer _____

b. herbivores _____, _____

c. carnivore _____

4. In the situation above, the relationship between the hippo and the open-bill stork is one of _____. Circle the correct answer.

a. predator-prey   **c.** parasitism

b. commensalism   **d.** producer-consumer

Problem Solving

5. Suppose you are camping at a state park. On a separate sheet of paper predict three biotic factors and three abiotic factors that you are likely to find when you pitch your tent.

Name _____ Date _____

6. Suppose a new shopping mall is being built in a large field near your home. Explain how this might affect the biotic and abiotic factors of the field ecosystem.

_____

_____

_____

Word Power

Circle the letter of each correct answer.

7. The interactions shown in this picture are all examples of _____ .

   a. symbiosis

   b. predator-prey relationships

   c. photosynthesis

   d. decomposition

8. Other than the earthworms, all of the other animals are

   a. producers   **c.** carnivores

   b. herbivores   **d.** prey

9. Organisms that use the Sun to carry on photosynthesis are _____ .

   a. producers   **c.** herbivores

   b. consumers   **d.** omnivores

10. Which living things in an ecosystem play the biggest role in helping rotting leaves become soil?

   a. carnivores   **c.** decomposers

   b. producers   **d.** herbivores

Name _____ Date _____

1. Label the ocean food web using the terms from the box.

first-order consumer	**second-order consumer**
decomposer	**third-order consumer**
producer	**third- and fourth-order consumer**

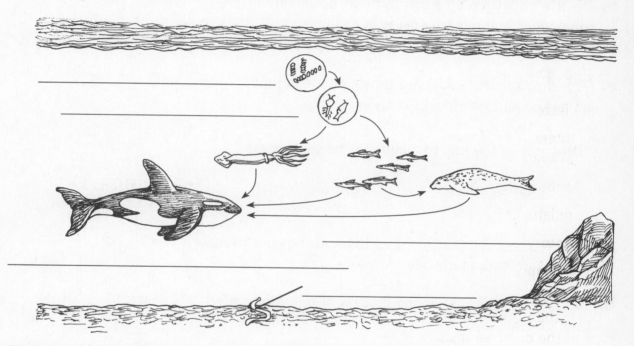

2. Under each term below, write an example of an organism from a marsh ecosystem that completes the food chain.

Producer → First-order → Second-order → Third-order → Decomposer
            consumer   consumer   consumer

_____   _____   _____   _____   _____

Process Skills
Inferring, Communicating

In the Arctic Circle, caribou search for patches of mosses and lichens. The caribou are watched by grey wolves that prey on sick or weak animals. What are the producers in this ecosystem, and how does their number compare to the number of first- and second-order consumers?

CHAPTER 2

Name _____ Date _____

1. Circle the correct word to complete the sentences.

a. The (life cycle, water cycle, carbon-dioxide oxygen cycle) is the constant movement of water in a continuous cycle through land, sea, air and living things.

b. The use of oxygen by a cell to break down carbon compounds and release energy is called (cell respiration, transpiration, precipitation).

c. (Proteins, sugars, acids) are the compounds that act as the building blocks of living things.

2. Use the words in the box to complete the sentences.

photosynthesis	cell respiration	transpiration

a. During _____, living things use oxygen and release carbon dioxide.

b. _____ is the process of releasing water through leaves.

c. During _____, plants take in carbon dioxide and release oxygen.

Process Skills
Observing, Experimenting

Patti placed a plant inside a plastic bag. A day later she observed droplets on the inside of the bag. Then she removed a leaf and put it in a test tube with yellow BTB solution. She observed that the solution turned blue when the test tube was left in sunlight. The solution remained yellow in a second test tube containing BTB but no leaf. What two forms of matter has Patti observed being recycled by her plant? What plant processes have taken place? Why did Patti use the second test tube? Write your answers on a separate sheet of paper.

© Silver Burdett Ginn

Name _____ Date _____

Analyze Information

1. In the picture below, circle the source of energy for the ecosystem. Then draw arrows to show how energy flows from the source, to the producer, and to the first-order consumer.

For questions 2–3, circle the letter of the correct answer.

2. How much of the energy stored in the producer will be available to the first-order consumer who uses it for food?

   a. all of it   **c.** about 50 percent of it

   b. none of it   **d.** less than 10 percent of it

3. Fran placed a test tube containing a green leaf and yellow BTB solution in the sunlight. A few minutes later she observed the solution turn a blue color. How can you explain what happened?

   a. Oxygen was used by the leaf.   **c.** Water was used by the leaf.

   b. Carbon dioxide was used by the leaf.   **d.** The leaf decomposed.

4. What is the difference between a food chain and a food web?

_____

_____

_____

Name _____ Date _____

Problem Solving

5. One farmer started growing forest mushrooms on oak logs. The other planted a field of alfalfa. Alfalfa roots are the home of nitrogen-fixing bacteria. Both farmers were helping certain kinds of matter get recycled in the ecosystem. Can you explain how?

_____

_____

_____

6. List the foods you have eaten in one meal today. Explain what kind of consumer you are for each of the foods consumed.

_____

_____

Word Power

In items 7–10, circle the letter of each correct answer.

7. The process in the water cycle in which liquid water changes to water vapor is _____.

a. evaporation   **b.** cell respiration   **c.** photosynthesis   **d.** precipitation

8. The _____ includes bacteria that help supply matter needed to make proteins.

a. water cycle

b. carbon dioxide-oxygen cycle

c. nitrogen cycle

d. hydrogen cycle

9. Spider monkeys in tree branches overhead in a rain forest use the stored energy in food, which is released by _____.

a. photosynthesis   **b.** cell respiration   **c.** the water cycle   **d.** transpiration

10. Monkeys that feed on the trees of the rain forest are _____.

a. herbivores

b. carnivores

c. predators

d. producers

Name _____ Date _____

1. Fill in the blanks using the terms in the box.

biomes	deciduous forests	desert	rain forests	tundra

Let's take an imaginary trip around the world by thinking about the world's largest ecosystems, or _____. In the warmest climates, there are lush _____, where it rains almost every day. What a contrast to the _____, which can also be very hot, but where it hardly rains at all. Farther north, the _____, grow. There the winters are cold, but the summers are warm and wet. Even farther north are the taiga, where you find coniferous forests, and the _____, where the subsoil stays frozen all year.

2. Write the name of the biome each of these organisms would call home.

_____ _____ _____ _____ _____

Process Skills
Inferring

Several students were watering some of their classroom plants on the schedule shown. Can you infer what kind of plants are in each group? Write your answer on a separate sheet of paper.

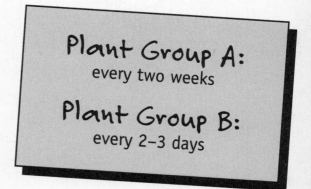

Plant Group A:
every two weeks

Plant Group B:
every 2–3 days

Name _____ Date _____

1. Match each term on the left with its definition on the right.

   a. biodiversity   species that are gone forever

   b. threatened   abundance of different life forms

   c. endangered   species in danger of becoming endangered

   d. extinct   species in danger of becoming extinct

2. Suppose you are a newspaper reporter. On a separate sheet of paper, write a headline and a few sentences about the loss of species from the rain forest. Use words such as biodiversity, endangered, extinct, and threatened.

Process Skills
Communicating, Making a Hypothesis

Hypothesize what has happened to the rain forest of the Philippines. What do you think has happened to the many species of birds and flowering plants that lived in the original rain forest? Write your answer on a separate sheet of paper.

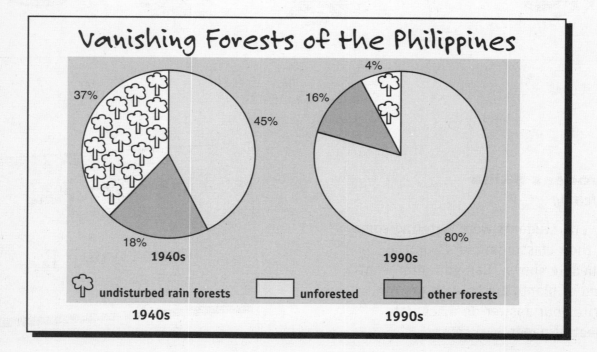

Vanishing Forests of the Philippines

37%   45%

18%

1940s

4%

16%   80%

1990s

🌲 undisturbed rain forests   ☐ unforested   ▨ other forests

1940s   **1990s**

Name _____ Date _____

Analyze Information

1. Fill in the two missing biomes on the rainfall table.

Biome	Yearly Rainfall
Tundra	less than 25 cm
Taiga	35 to 75 cm
Deciduous forest	75 to 125 cm
	more than 200 cm
Grassland	25 to 75 cm
	less than 25 cm

2. The terms endangered, extinct, and threatened help describe the loss of species. Write these terms in order of increasing risk of a species vanishing.

_____

3. Which abiotic factor in a biome is closely dependent

on the latitude? _____

4. The pie graph shows Earth's water. Shade in the portion of the pie graph that represents the approximate amount of water in lakes, rivers, and streams.

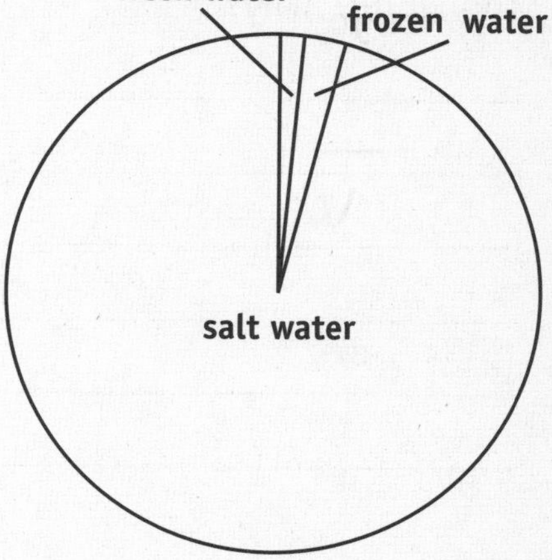

Word Power

Circle the letter of each correct answer.

5. Which type of forest contains mainly maples, oak, ash, and birch trees?

a. tropical rain forest

c. deciduous forest

b. coniferous forest

d. taiga

6. If an area has fir, spruce, and pine trees and the winters are cold, you are probably in a ____.

a. taiga   **b.** tundra   **c.** grassland   **d.** desert

7. The largest saltwater ecosystem is the ____.

a. shoreline   **c.** open ocean

b. coastal ocean   **d.** delta

8. A species that is near extinction is said to be ____.

a. threatened   **b.** endangered   **c.** exotic   **d.** abiotic

Problem Solving

9. What is the greatest threat to biodiversity of biomes all over the world? Why?

_____

_____

_____

_____

_____

_____

10. Why is biodiversity important to all people?

_____

_____

_____

_____

_____

Name _____ Date _____

PREDATOR ISLAND
· ·

Play a game about a predator-prey relationship. Use colored beans to represent the predator and prey populations that live in an imaginary ecosystem called Predator Island.

Materials

✔ two colors of dried beans in separate containers
✔ one empty container
✔ tray

✔ 16 index cards
✔ markers
✔ graph paper
✔ 2 colored pencils

Procedure

1. With your partners, choose a predator-prey relationship. Decide in which biome the relationship would be found. Write a brief description of your Predator Island.

2. Decide who will do each task on the Task List. If you are the *Census Taker,* choose which color bean will represent the predator and which color the prey. Count out 50 beans into piles of 10. Place them on one side of the tray to represent the prey. Place 5 predator beans on the opposite side of the tray. Mark the empty container KILLED for predator and prey that are killed. If you are the *Dealer,* make 10 Circle of Life Cards by drawing a circle on 10 index cards. The Circle of Life Cards represent typical feeding interactions and reproductive cycles. Then make 6 Environment Cards by choosing 6 events that would affect the populations. For example, a card could say: "Plentiful food supply. Prey population increases by 20 and predator by 2." If you are the *Record Keeper,* you will keep a tally of the number of predators and prey alive after each turn. Make a line graph with rounds of play on the bottom axis and the number in each population on the vertical axis. Use different colored pencils to show the different populations.

Name _____ Date _____

3. Once you have completed your individual tasks, start the game! The Dealer and Census Taker decide who will be the predator and who will be the prey. The Predator draws the first card. With each card, the Record Keeper will graph the populations. When you have completed several turns, look at the graph and discuss it.

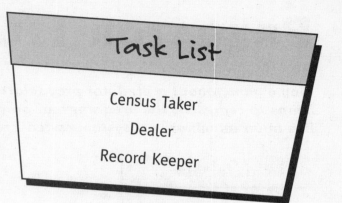

Task List

Census Taker

Dealer

Record Keeper

Predator Island Game Rules

1. To set up, place 5 predator beans and 50 prey beans on opposite sides of the tray. Shuffle together the 10 Circle of Life Cards and 6 Environment Cards and place them face down.

2. The player who represents the predator draws the first card. If the player draws a Circle of Life Card, each predator bean captures and eats a prey. The eaten prey go into the container marked KILLED. If the player draws an Environment Card, whatever the card says affects that turn.

3. The player who represents the prey draws the next card. If it is a Circle of Life Card, the prey population increases by 5. Add 5 prey beans. If the player draws an Environment Card, whatever the card says affects that turn.

4. The Record Keeper counts how many there are of each population after each card is drawn. Those numbers are marked on the graph.

5. The players keep taking turns until all the cards are used or until one of the populations gets to zero.

PREDATOR ISLAND

Students choose several ecology subconcepts that show an understanding of how environmental conditions can affect a predator-prey relationship.

1. Get Ready

Time: 50 minutes

Grouping: Groups of 3

Collaborative Strategy: You may wish to suggest that students work in groups of six, with two students working on each task. To assess cooperative learning skills, use the Group Skills Checklist provided in this book.

Materials: (each student)
- two colors of dried beans in separate containers
- one empty container
- tray
- 16 index cards
- markers
- graph paper
- 2 colored pencils

2. Guide the Procedure

Explain to students that they are going to play a game that will allow them to demonstrate what they have learned about ecosystems and populations. Allow 10 minutes for them to decide on the predator-prey relationship, and 15 minutes to set up the beans, write the cards, and set up the graphs. They can play the game and discuss the results for the remaining 20–25 minutes.

As students are working, move from group to group, observing performance and answering questions. You may wish to offer assistance in setting up and using the population graph. The Record Keeper may make two separate graphs instead of a double-line graph. At the end of the activity, invite students to share their cards and graphs. Afterwards, gather students' worksheets, graphs, and cards so that they can be scored.

3. Assess Performance

Use the scoring rubric to help you evaluate students' work.
- Have students created a model that shows an understanding of how environmental factors affect a predator-prey relationship?
- Have students made valid decisions in choosing and writing the Environment Cards?
- Have students accurately recorded their data on the graphs?

UNIT **D**

Name _____ Date _____

PREDATOR ISLAND

Concept: The populations of predators and prey fluctuate according to changes in the environment.

Assessed items	Point	What to look for
Choice of predator-prey relationship and biome	3	Students chose a relationship that fits the criteria and identified the correct biome.
	2	The predator-prey relationship is indicated, but the biome is not correctly identified or described.
	1	The predator-prey relationship and biome are unclear or missing.
Task Option 1: Census Taker	3	The *Census Taker* accurately disperses the beans.
	2	The *Census Taker* attempts to accurately disperse the beans and participates in the activity.
	1	The *Census Taker* does not accurately disperse the beans.
Task Option 2: Dealer	3	The *Dealer* identifies many variables and shows understanding of the interaction of predator-prey relationships.
	2	The *Dealer* does not accurately represent the interaction of predator-prey relationships.
	1	The work of the *Dealer* is unclear or incomplete.
Task Option 3: Record Keeper	3	The *Record Keeper* makes a graph that reflects changes in each population as the consequence of each playing card, and relates changes on the graph to specific environmental events.
	2	The Record Keeper's graph is for the most part accurate and correctly relates most changes to specific environmental events.
	1	The Record Keeper's graph is incorrect or incomplete.

Name _____ Date _____

Analyze Information

Use the picture below to answer questions 1–6.

1. The animals and plants in this picture belong to which ecosystem? ____

    a. salt marsh   **c.** desert

    b. deciduous forest   **d.** tundra

2. If you counted all the shrews in this environment, you would then know ____.

    a. the producers of this biome   **c.** the shrew population

    b. an ecosystem   **d.** all the carnivores

3. What organisms in this ecosystem are consumers? Explain your choices.

_____

_____

4. How would you compare the biodiversity of species in this ecosystem to that of a rain forest?

_____

Name _____ Date _____

5. The anteater uses its long sticky tongue to invade a termite nest for a meal. Many termites eat wood. Make a simple food chain below to show these interactions.

_____

6. Suppose a deciduous forest experienced a long-term drop in yearly rainfall. What biomes might replace the deciduous forest?

_____

_____

For questions 7 and 8, circle the letter of the correct answer.

7. When the processes of transpiration, evaporation, and precipitation take place, what kind of matter is recycled in the biosphere?

a. nitrogen   **c.** carbon dioxide

b. water   **d.** oxygen

8. Which of these processes is part of the carbon dioxide oxygen cycle?

a. nitrogen fixation   **c.** transpiration

b. precipitation   **d.** cell respiration

Problem Solving

9. There are an increasing number of endangered species. What do you think is happening to the habitat of most endangered animals?

_____

_____

_____

_____

Name _____ Date _____

10. The number of deer, raccoons, skunks, and Canada geese are on the rise. Scientists worry that these kinds of animals are taking over at the expense of other animals in the same environment. Why, do you think, are these animals doing so well?

_____

_____

_____

_____

11. Some people think that eating "low on the food chain" is both more healthful and better for the environment than eating "high on the food chain." What do you think these expressions mean? Why might eating "low" not necessarily be good?

_____

_____

_____

_____

12. Why should the plant biodiversity around the world be protected?

_____

_____

_____

_____

Name _____ Date _____

13. Suppose you are in charge of raising money to save an ecosystem. What slogan would you put on a poster for your cause that would state your case dramatically?

_____

_____

_____

_____

Word Power

Write the term from the box on the line following its definition.

taiga	parasite	producer	mutualism
community	herbivore	threatened species	

14. a group of organisms that may soon be endangered _____

15. an organism that feeds off another organism _____

16. organism that makes its own food _____

17. long term relationship in which both organisms benefit _____

18. biome in which coniferous forests are found _____

19. all the living populations of an ecosystem _____

20. plant eater _____

Name _____ **Date** _____

1. Match each definition on the left with a word or phrase on the right.

    a. a measure of how easily a mineral can be scratched   streak

    b. the way minerals reflect light   hardness

    c. a property that describes how some minerals break   diamond

    d. the color of a powdered mineral   luster

    e. the hardest mineral   cleavage

2. Mark wants to place six minerals in an egg carton so that the minerals with metallic luster are in the top row and those with nonmetallic luster are in the bottom row. Also, he wants to place them in order of increasing hardness. Hardness numbers are shown in parentheses. Using the information given, label his carton with the correct letters.

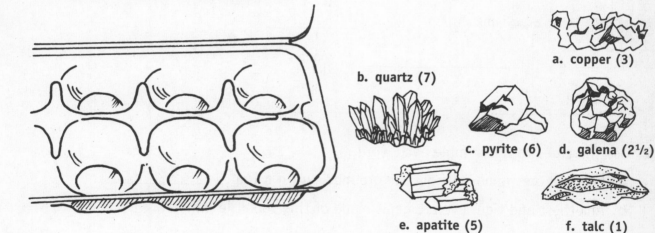

a. copper (3)

b. quartz (7)

c. pyrite (6)　　d. galena (2½)

e. apatite (5)

f. talc (1)

Process Skills
Classifying

Gerry observed some properties of an unknown mineral specimen. He wrote his data in the chart shown. How did he test for hardness?

Color	Luster	Hardness
clear	nonmetallic (glassy)	H > glass H < topaz (7 on Mohs' scale)

_____

_____

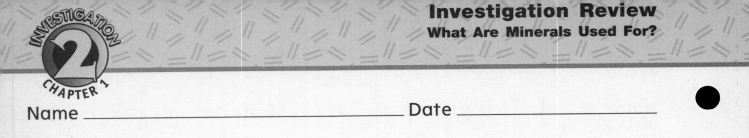
Name _____ Date _____

1. Use the words in the box to complete the concept map.

steel	**computer chips**	**concrete**	**glass**
minerals	**magnetite**	**hematite**	**recycled**
iron	**quartz**		

Some important _____ are

_____ _____ and _____ ores _____ to
extend our use of
mineral resources

used in building
materials

heated
to make

separated into
oxygen and
silicon to make

are smelted
to get

_____

made
into

_____

_____ _____

_____

2. Use the clues to unscramble each word.

  a. How are ores removed from the ground? g i n n i m _____

  b. Amethyst and tiger eye are gems made of this versatile mineral.

  z a r t q u _____

  c. This is something that grows, but it's not alive. l a s t c r y _____

  d. How are ores treated to remove metal? l e t m s g i n _____

Process Skills
Communicating, Inferring

Which property of mineral quartz makes it useful for making
concrete? Which property allows it to be made into glass?
Write your answer on a separate sheet of paper.

Name _____ Date _____

Analyze Information

For questions 1–3, circle the letter of the correct answer.

1. Suppose you run a factory in the northwestern part of the United States. You want to buy copper only from a major producing area in the U.S. Use the map to decide where to get the copper. The circles show the locations of copper-producing areas.

Canada

U.S.

Mexico

a. from eastern United States

c. from western United States

b. from western Canada

d. from Mexico

2. The diagram below shows the steps involved in converting iron ore into steel. Suppose you wanted to make an old-fashioned iron school bell. What method would you use?

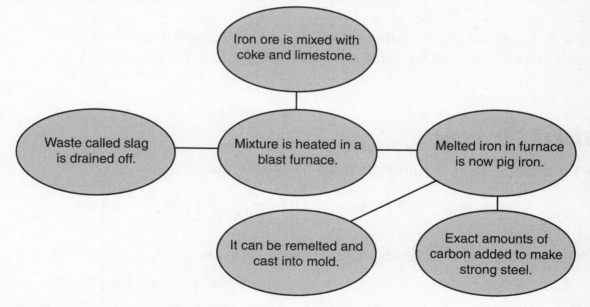

Iron ore is mixed with coke and limestone.

Waste called slag is drained off.

Mixture is heated in a blast furnace.

Melted iron in furnace is now pig iron.

It can be remelted and cast into mold.

Exact amounts of carbon added to make strong steel.

a. Drain some slag from a blast furnace and cast it into a bell shape.

c. Remelt pig iron and cast it into a bell mold.

b. Heat iron ore in a blast furnace and cast it into a bell mold.

d. Add carbon to pig iron then cast it into a bell mold.

Name _____ Date _____

3. You have mineral samples of gold and pyrite, known as "fool's gold." In the space at the right, draw what each mineral's streak would look like on a streak plate and label the color.

Problem Solving

4. Mineral resources are nonrenewable. How can you help to conserve dwindling mineral resources?

_____

_____

5. You have an unknown metallic mineral that does not scratch quartz. It does scratch talc. List the three minerals in order of increasing hardness.

_____

Word Power

Use the words in the box to complete the paragraph below.

cleavage	hardness	luster	ore	streak

Trisha tested a mineral to identify it. It had a metallic _____ and produced a distinctive _____ on a piece of tile. She used the scratch test to find the _____ of the mineral and checked for _____ planes. She determined that the mineral was a lead _____ known as galena.

Name _____ Date _____

1. Draw a line from each type of rock in the left column to the phrase that explains its origin in the right column.

a. igneous rocks   form from small bits of rocks and minerals that become cemented by natural processes

b. sedimentary rocks   form when pre-existing rocks are changed by heat, pressure, or chemicals

c. metamorphic rocks   form when hot, melted material cools and hardens

2. Write the answer to each riddle on the line provided.

a. Deep within Earth I'm called magma, but once I reach the surface I'm known as _____.

b. I depend on how long it takes for the minerals within a rock to form. I am the rock's _____.

c. I have been trapped in this piece of limestone for ages—even before it was a rock! I help scientists learn about organisms from the past. I am a _____.

Process Skills
Classifying, Inferring

Suppose you have two igneous rocks containing mostly light-colored minerals. One has large mineral grains. The other has small grains. Classify and identify the two rocks using the data provided. Which rock took a longer time to form? How do you know? Which formed closer to Earth's surface? Write your answer on a separate sheet of paper.

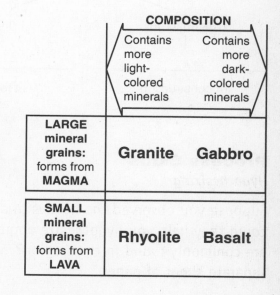

COMPOSITION		
	Contains more light-colored minerals	Contains more dark-colored minerals
LARGE mineral grains: forms from **MAGMA**	**Granite**	**Gabbro**
SMALL mineral grains: forms from **LAVA**	**Rhyolite**	**Basalt**

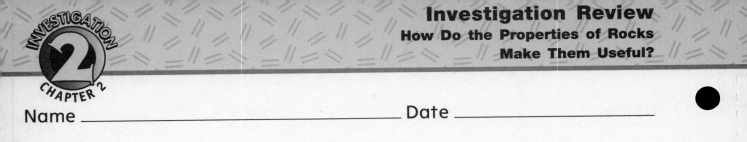

Name _____ Date _____

1. Use the words in the box to complete the sentences.

clay	dimension stone	marble	quarries
crushed stone	firing	molds	water

Each year, billions of tons of rock are removed from _____

all over the world. Most of the rock leaves a quarry as _____. Some

rock, known as _____, remains in larger pieces. Granite used in a

building and a _____ countertop are examples of dimension stone.

Many buildings are made of brick. Unlike rocks, bricks are made by people. The

"recipe" is pretty simple. _____ minerals and _____are mixed

into a thick paste. The mixture is put into rectangular _____ and placed in

an oven. _____ the bricks makes them harder.

2. Fill in the blanks of the concept map.

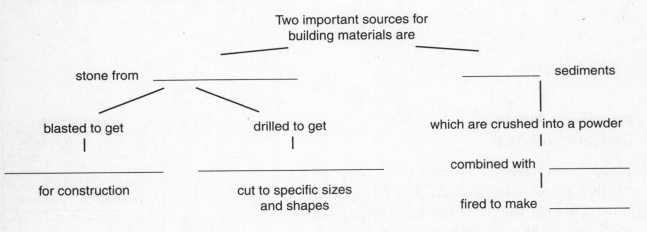

Process Skills
Hypothesizing

Suppose you observed the houses in a very old village. How could they help you hypothesize about the types of rocks that are commonly found in that region? Write your answer on a separate sheet of paper.

Name _____ Date _____

1. Use the words in the box to identify each type of coal described below.

anthracite	bituminous	lignite	peat

a. Temperature and pressure increase and squeeze most of the water from lignite to form _____ coal.

b. Swamp plants decay and form a dark, watery material called _____.

c. Metamorphism changes bituminous coal into _____, the coal with the highest percentage of carbon.

d. Sediments squeeze much of the water out of peat, forming _____.

2. Complete the diagram of the rock cycle.

Process Skills
Communicating

List the steps involved to change an igneous rock into a sedimentary rock. Write or draw your answer on a separate sheet of paper.

Name _____ Date _____

Analyze Information

1. You examine a piece of granite without a magnifying glass. You see relatively large mineral grains. Hypothesize how the crystals formed.

_____

_____

2. Suppose you find a rock. You can see thin, flat layers that feel smooth to the touch. Use this part of the rock key to identify the rock. Circle the correct name.

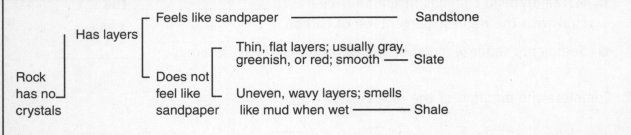

3. The map shows the New England states that are well known for their rock quarries. From looking at this map, which of the following statements is probably true? Circle the letter of the correct answer.

a. Much of the rock quarried in New England is igneous rock.

b. Granite changes into marble.

c. Most of the rock in the region is sedimentary in origin.

d. Shale is the only sedimentary rock found in the region.

4. Suppose you are planning a building and want to use granite dimension stone and marble flooring. Which state

could supply both? _____

© Silver Burdett Ginn

Name _____ Date _____

Problem Solving

5. On a separate sheet of paper, draw a model of the rock cycle. Use clay, basalt, slate and shale.

6. In one part of Anytown, U.S.A. there are three houses. One is made of brick, one of concrete, and one of dimension stone. Describe how these raw materials are produced. Write your answer on a separate sheet of paper.

Word Power

Answer each question with a word from the box.

cementation	quarry	magma	rock cycle

7. What do we call a mine, usually close to or at Earth's surface, from which certain rocks are removed? _____

8. What is the series of changes that rocks undergo? _____

9. What is the binding of sediments called? _____

10. What is the name given to molten rock material that forms deep within Earth?

_____

INVESTIGATION 1 CHAPTER 3

Name _____ Date _____

1. If you took an imaginary journey to the center of Earth, your log might read something like this. Fill in the blanks using the words in the box.

crust	iron	mantle	oceans	plates	
inner	magma	Moho	outer	solid	

Day 1: Today we cut through the rocky _____, which is much thicker on land than under the _____. This layer, with the upper mantle, is broken into _____.

Day 2: We passed through a boundary known as the _____ and into Earth's _____. It is made of igneous rock, which sometimes rises toward the crust as _____.

Day 3: We have reached the _____ core of Earth. It is so hot that _____ and nickel are liquids.

Day 4: Finally! We've reached the _____ core. It is almost as hot as the Sun. The pressure here compressed melted metals into a _____ core.

Day 5: Back home at last.

2. Suppose you could make a slice through Earth. Draw a diagram of what it would look like and label the four main layers.

Process Skills
Making a Model

Suppose you had brown, yellow, orange, and red clay. Which colors would you use to make a model of the layers of Earth? What characteristics would you represent with each color? For which color clay would you need the greatest quantity? Write your answer on a separate sheet of paper.

© Silver Burdett Ginn

Name _____ Date _____

1. On the line under each set of terms, write what the terms have in common.

   a. imprint, cast, mold

   _____

   b. using index fossils, using potassium-argon decay

   _____

2. Read the stages that describe how a plant might become a fossil. Number the stages in the order in which they would occur.

   _____ The rock containing the fossil is eroded and exposed.

   _____ The plant is buried by sediments. Over time, the leaves decay, but leave an imprint in the soft sediment.

   _____ The plant dies.

   _____ Eventually the woody parts are replaced with minerals that harden to become rock.

Process Skills
Inferring

Imagine that you find two different rocks on your way home from school. They both contain the same kind of trilobite. What can you infer about the age of these two rocks? Is your inference a relative age or an absolute age? Explain.

_____

_____

_____

_____

© Silver Burdett Ginn

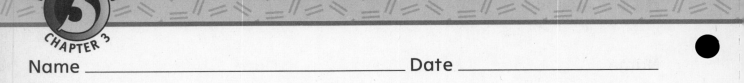
Name _____ Date _____

1. Draw a line to connect each term on the left with its definition on the right.

a. fold   the removal of weathered rock

b. anticline   a downward fold in rocks

c. syncline   a mountain formed when rock layers
                             are pushed up by magma

d. erosion   an upward fold in rocks

e. dome   a bend in a rock layer

2. Use the words in the box to complete the crossword puzzle.

weathering	plates	wind	ridges
anticline	hogbacks	folds	dome

Down

1. Process that breaks rocks down into sediments

3. Rocks resistant to erosion form these

6. Bends in rock

Across

2. Formed when rock layers are pushed up by magma

4. Upward rock fold

5. Pieces of Earth's crust and upper mantle

7. A force that causes erosion

8. Another name for steep ridges

Process Skills
Inferring, Communicating

Imagine you are riding in a car. You pass some exposed rock layers made visible by blasting. The layers are in the shape of a wave. Why?

Name _____ Date _____

1. Fill in the blanks using the words from the box.

faults	horizontal	earthquakes
fault-block	vertical	strike-slip

On a trip to California, you can learn a lot about _____, which are breaks in rocks along which movement occurs. When the movement along some faults is _____, _____ mountains can form. The Sierra Nevada Mountains are spectacular examples of this kind of mountain. Near the coast of California is the famous San Andreas fault. The movement along this fault is _____, and it is known as a _____ fault. Each year the city of Los Angeles moves several centimeters north toward San Francisco. There have been many _____ along this fault.

2. When moving plates caused rocks in the Grand Canyon area to stretch, many normal faults were formed. The picture shows a normal fault. Label the fault line and draw arrows to show its movement.

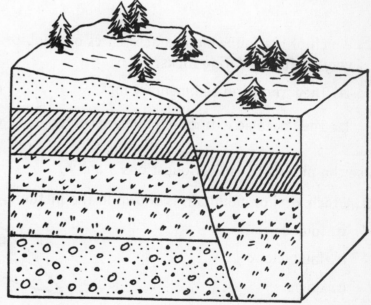

Process Skills
Making a Model

If you were holding a stack of books in each hand, how could you use them to show motion along a strike-slip fault? Write or draw your answer on a separate sheet of paper.

Name _____ Date _____

Analyze Information

For questions 1–4, circle the letter of the correct answer.

Use the diagram to answer questions 1 and 2. Suppose these horizontal rock layers were uncovered in an ancient seabed where they have been relatively undisturbed. The middle layer contains trilobites that lived 500 to 600 million years ago.

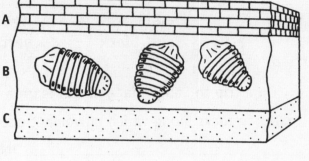

1. Which of the following can you infer about the ages of the rock layers?

   a. The absolute age of layer A is 600 million years old.

   b. Layer A is the oldest and Layer C the youngest.

   c. Layer B is the same age as layer A.

   d. Layer C is older than 600 million years old.

2. Which of the following characteristics of trilobites makes them very useful for dating rocks?

   a. They formed in sedimentary rock.

   c. Their fossils are plentiful.

   b. They became extinct relatively recently.

   d. They can undergo metamorphism.

Use the picture to answer questions 3 and 4.

3. Which kind of mountain is shown in the picture?

   a. folded

   b. fault-block

   c. dome

   d. Black Hill

4. Movement that caused this mountain to form was probably _____.

   a. along a normal fault   **c.** along the Moho

   b. along a strike-slip fault   **d.** at the epicenter

Name _____ Date _____

Problem Solving

5. This diagram shows what some rocks look like. You know that limestone and shale wear away easily, but sandstone and conglomerates resist erosion. Draw what the rocks must have looked like long ago.

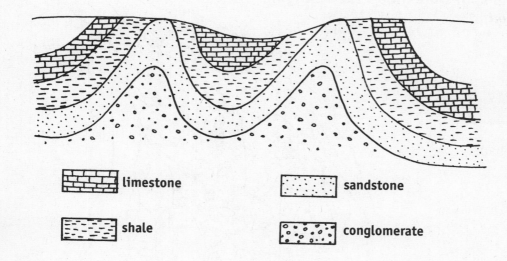

 limestone   sandstone

shale   conglomerate

6. Scientists know worms were some of the first creatures on Earth. How might worms leave evidence of their existence?

_____

_____

_____

Word Power

Fill in the blanks using the words from the box.

core	crust	mantle	model

A _____ of Earth's interior shows a layered structure. The thickest layer, the _____, lies just beneath the _____, which is the thinnest layer. The _____ is believed to be made up mostly of iron and nickel.

© Silver Burdett Ginn

UNIT
E

Name _____ Date _____

ALONG THE ROCK KEY ROAD
··

You and your partner are going on an imaginary trip.
You'll be looking for a spot that shows the changing
nature of Earth's crust.

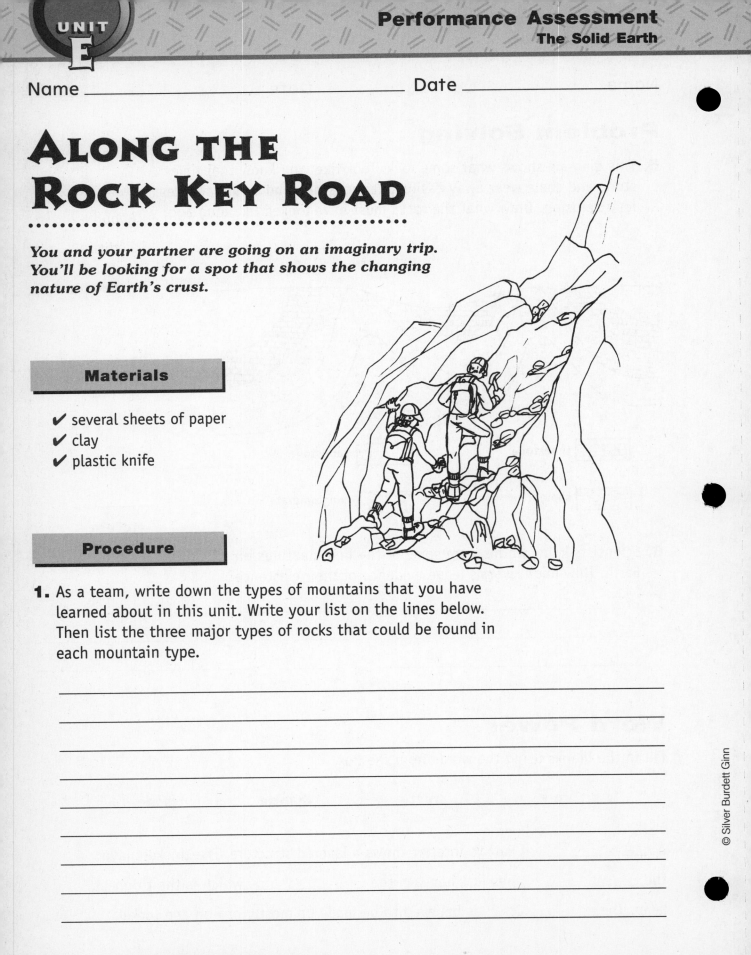

Materials

✔ several sheets of paper
✔ clay
✔ plastic knife

Procedure

1. As a team, write down the types of mountains that you have
learned about in this unit. Write your list on the lines below.
Then list the three major types of rocks that could be found in
each mountain type.

_____

_____

_____

_____

_____

_____

_____

_____

Name _____ Date _____

2. Look at the task list with your partner. Decide which of you will do each task. You can ask for help from your partner on your task, but you are in charge of completing it. On the line below, list the task you've chosen. In the Along the Rock Key Road Data Space, record your data. If you choose *Be a Rock-hound*, describe the kind of rocks that may be found in each kind of moun-

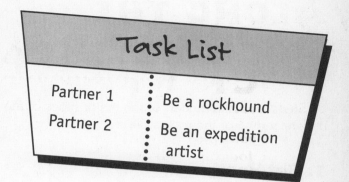

tain. Be prepared to demonstrate how each rock type fits into the rock cycle by making a drawing. If you choose *Expedition Artist,* make a paper or clay model of the rock layers of each kind of mountain. Show how the rock layers may have looked before and after the geological events that formed them.

Task _____

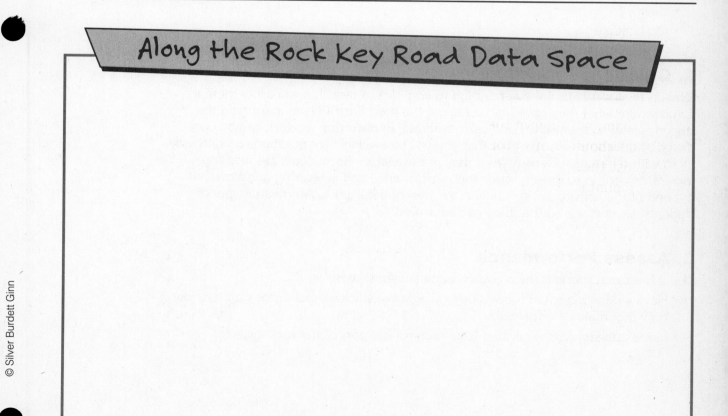

Along the Rock Key Road Data Space

ALONG THE ROCK KEY ROAD

Students make models of the major types of mountains and demonstrate an understanding of the rock cycle.

1. Get Ready

Time: 50 Minutes

Grouping: Pairs

Collaborative Strategy: You may wish to suggest that students work in groups of four, with two students working together on each task. To assess cooperative learning skills, use the Group Skills Checklist provided in this book.

Materials: (each station)
- several sheets of paper
- clay
- plastic knife

2. Guide the Procedure

Explain to students that they are going to complete a task that will allow them to demonstrate what they have learned about the solid Earth. Have them read the student pages to themselves and ask questions. Explain that the task can be completed at their work stations, but that you will be available for questions and provide them with different rock samples if they are available. As students are working, move from group to group, observing performance and answering questions. At the end of the activity, invite students to present their work. Afterwards, gather students' worksheets so that they can be scored.

3. Assess Performance

Use the scoring rubric to help you evaluate students' work.
- Have students created models using diagrams, stacks of paper, or clay to show how mountains are formed?
- Have students communicated how each rock is part of the rock cycle?

Name _____ Date _____

ALONG THE ROCK KEY ROAD
···

Concept: Students should clearly list the types of mountains and three rock types based on an understanding of the rock cycle and the processes involved in mountain building.

Assessed items	Points	What to look for
Lists of Mountains and Rocks	3	Mountains and rock types are clearly indicated.
	2	The list does not show an understanding of which rocks are likely to be found at each mountain.
	1	Mountain and rock types are unclear or missing.
Task—Option 1: Be a Rockhound	3	The Rockhound clearly explains how rock types are related in the rock cycle.
	2	The Rockhound correctly describes either the rock types or the rock cycle, but not both.
	1	The work of the Rockhound is unclear or incomplete.
Task—Option 2: Expedition Artist	3	The Expedition Artist uses paper or clay to demonstrate how each kind of mountain forms.
	2	Some part of the model is inaccurate.
	1	The model is unclear or incomplete.
Oral Presentation	3	Student shows good preparation.
	2	Student's responses are adequate.
	1	Student's responses show that he or she is unprepared.

Name _____ Date _____

Analyze Information

For items 1–2, circle the letter of the correct answer.

1. Which mineral property is shown at the right?

   a. cleavage   **c.** color

   b. luster   **d.** streak

2. Which kind of coal has the greatest percentage of carbon and gives off the most heat when burned?

   a. peat   **b.** lignite

   c. bituminous coal   **d.** anthracite

3. Anna is gathering data on her crystal growth experiments. She has not yet drawn in the last bar on her graph. What do you predict it will look like? Draw it on the graph.

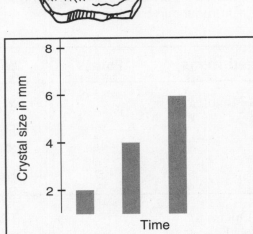

4. This wedge represents part of Earth. Label the layers.

5. Circle the term that doesn't belong with the other three. Explain why that term is different.

   granite   brick   obsidian   gabbro

_____

_____

_____

Name _____ Date _____

6. The map shows the San Andreas fault, which is a plate boundary. The arrow shows the direction in which the the Pacific Plate is moving. What kind of fault is shown? _____

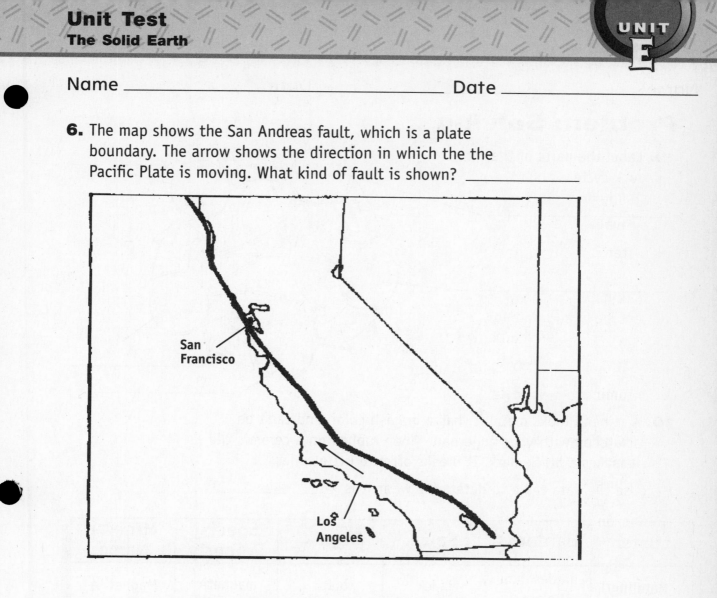

7. Describe the kind of movement that occurs along the fault shown. Explain what happens when rocks on either side catch and lock.

_____

_____

8. Using the map above as a guide, which of these statements is most likely to be true? Circle the correct answer.

a. In a million years, San Francisco might be as far south as Los Angeles.

b. In 10 million years, Los Angeles might be under water.

c. In 10 million years, Los Angeles might be directly west of San Francisco.

d. The two plates might combine into one large plate.

Name _____ Date _____

Problem Solving

9. Label the parts of the rock cycle.

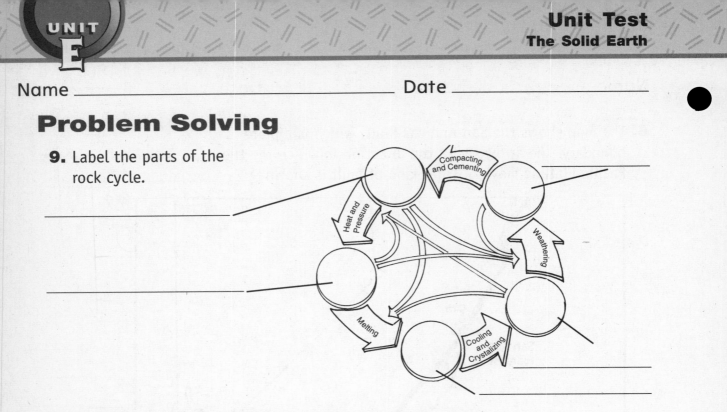

10. A mineral looks metallic, has a grayish color, and can't be scratched with your fingernail. When rubbed on a ceramic tile, it makes a black mark. It breaks off into little cubes.

Use the data table to determine what it is. _____

Luster	Hardness	Color	Streak	Special Property	Mineral Name
Metallic	harder than glass	black	black	magnetic	Magnetite
Metallic	harder than glass	brassy yellow	black	fool's gold	Pyrite
Metallic	softer than glass	steel gray	red or reddish brown	reddish patches	Hematite
Metallic	harder than a fingernail	silver gray	gray to black	shows cubic cleavage	Galena

11. Scientists at a location far from an earthquake can receive P-waves but cannot receive S-waves from the quake. Explain.

_____

_____

_____

Name _____ Date _____

12. A team of scientists has uncovered a fossil bed. On the surface of the ground, it appears that 280 million-year-old ammonite shells are right next to 340 million-year-old fossils. Next to those fossils are ammonite shells that are only 230 million years old. Can you explain? Use an arrow on the art to clarify your explanation.

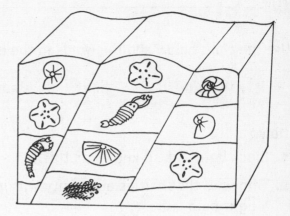

_____

_____

_____

_____

Word Power

Draw a line to match each term on the left with its definition on the right.

13. plate   breaking up of rock into sediments

14. weathering   change in rocks caused by heat and pressure

15. quartz   upward fold in rock layer

16. ore   moving segment of Earth's crust and upper mantle

17. index   rocks that are formed from magma or lava

18. anticline   mineral from which metal can be removed

19. igneous rocks   common mineral found in sand

20. metamorphism   kinds of fossils from species that were numerous over a short time

Investigation Review
What Is Light and
Where Does It Come From?

Name _____ Date _____

1. Use the clues below and the words in the box to complete the puzzle.

halogen	heat	filament	visible	UV light

Down

1. Black light is also known as this.

2. Thin wire that carries electricity within a light bulb

4. In many light bulbs, much energy is converted to this.

Across

3. Electromagnetic radiation we can see is called _____ light.

5. Very bright incandescent lamp

2. The words in each group are the same in some way. Explain what each word group has in common.

a. visible light, infrared radiation, ultraviolet radiation

_____

b. solar collectors, solar calculators, green plant cells

_____

c. fluorescent, incandescent, halogen

_____

Process Skills
Predicting, Commumicating

Your little sister tries to turn a toy flashlight on one evening, but it doesn't work. Which two parts should you check? How are the parts related? Write your answer on a separate sheet of paper.

Name _____ Date _____

1. Match each definition on the left with the correct word on the right.

    a. disturbance that moves away from its starting point   vacuum

    b. space that contains no matter   frequency

    c. distance from the crest of one wave to the crest of the next wave   wavelength

    d. number of waves produced each second   wave

2. Use the diagram below to answer the questions.

Electromagnetic Spectrum
Wavelength

longest ←   → shortest

| AM radio waves | TV FM waves | microwaves | infrared waves | visible light | ultraviolet rays | X-rays | gamma rays |

Frequency

lowest →   → highest

    a. Suppose you are looking at a red light. Indicate with an X where red light fits into the electromagnetic spectrum.

    b. What are two things that are the same about all the waves shown in the diagram?

    _____

    c. What are two things that differ from one part of the electromagnetic spectrum to another?

    _____

Process Skills
Inferring

Light and sound are both waves. Why do you think you always see lightning before you hear the thunder associated with it? Write you answer on a separate sheet of paper.

Name ______________________________ Date ____________________

1. Label the drawing using the words in the box.

plane mirror
reflected light ray
image
light ray

2. Use the clues to fill in the blanks. Then unscramble the circled letters to find the word that answers the riddle below.

a. another name for a flat mirror ___ (○) ___ ___ ___

b. light bouncing back from the surface of a mirror

___ ___ ___ ___ ___ ___ (○) ___ ___ ___

c. image caused by refraction of light above warm surfaces

___ ___ ___ ___ (○) ___

d. smooth reflecting surface

___ (○) ___ ___ ___ ___

e. where your image appears to be when you look into a plane mirror

___ ___ (○) ___ ___ ___

Riddle: What bends but doesn't break? ______________

Process Skills

Inferring

Suppose you want to buy a mirror to use on your bicycle to help you see images that are behind you while riding. What type of mirror—concave, convex, or plane—would you probably find in a bicycle shop? Explain your answer on a separate sheet of paper.

Name _____ Date _____

Analyze Information

1. Match the clues on the left with the correct word or phrase on the right.

    a. electromagnetic radiation that causes sunburn

    b. an intense beam of light that spreads out very little

    c. produced in heat lamps

    d. electromagnetic radiation with shortest wavelength

laser

infrared radiation

gamma rays

UV light

2. Circle the letter of the correct answer. Electromagnetic radiation from the Sun travels to Earth _____.

    a. as nuclear energy and heat

    b. by reflection and refraction

    c. as alternating waves

    d. in the vacuum of space

3. Draw on the diagram to show which part is a wavelength.

4. Which mirror should Shari use to see an enlarged image? Circle that mirror.

Name _____ Date _____

Problem Solving

5. Suppose you own a bicycle factory. Your employees will be
working night and day making bicycle parts. Would you install
incandescent or fluorescent lighting in your factory? Why?

_____

_____

6. On most cars, the passenger's side-view mirror is curved more than
the driver's side-view mirror. What kind of mirrors are used in side-
view mirrors? Why do you think the passenger mirror is curved more?

_____

_____

_____

Word Power

Circle the correct term within the parentheses to complete the
paragraph below.

On a trip to the supermarket, you can learn a lot about light. Your image may

be seen in overhead mirrors due to the (refraction, reflection, absorption) of

light. These mirrors have surfaces that curve outward and are called (plane,

concave, convex) mirrors. In the fluorescent lights on the ceiling, UV light is

changed to (visible light, gamma rays, black light). The different colors of light

differ in (wavelength, reflection, height).

© Silver Burdett Ginn

Name _____ Date _____

1. Fill in the blanks using the words in the box.

convex lens	farsighted	retina	focal point

A _____ is thin at the edges and thicker near the center.
The lens in the human eye is such a lens. It brings parallel light rays together at
the _____. A _____ person focuses images beyond the
retina. By wearing glasses with convex lenses, images are focused on the
_____, which allows the person to see clearly.

2. Label each type of lens shown below. Then draw arrows to show
what happens to light rays as they pass through each lens.

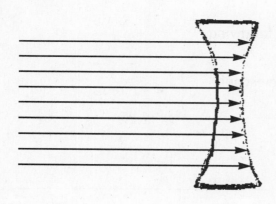

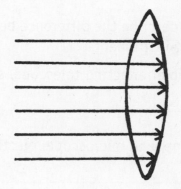

a. _____   b. _____

Process Skills
Observing, Classifying

How are concave lenses and convex lenses similar? What is the
main difference between how convex lenses and concave lenses
affect light? Write your answer on a separate sheet of paper.

Name _____ Date _____

1. Sequence the sentences below to describe the passage of light through a reflecting telescope.

A lens magnifies the star's image. Light from a star strikes a concave mirror. The star's image is reflected by a flat mirror.

_____

_____

2. How have microscopes helped increase our knowledge of the natural world?

_____

_____

_____

_____

3. Briefly describe the difference between each of the following pairs of instruments.

a. simple reflecting telescope, simple refracting telescope

_____

b. compound microscope, electron microscope

_____

Process Skills
Inferring

A friend is looking through a telescope at some distant trees. She says that the trees are upside down. Explain how the image has become inverted.

Name _____ Date _____

1. The picture below shows three projections of colored light.
Label the missing colors.

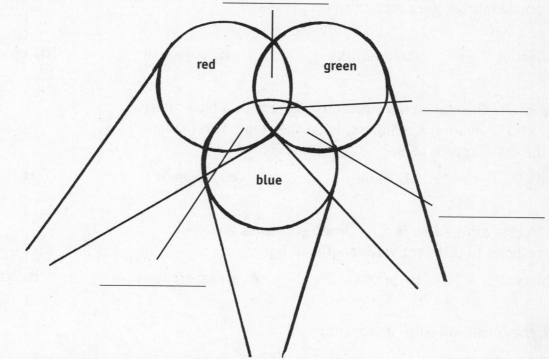

2. Write whether each item below is opaque, translucent,
or transparent.

    a. shallow water _____

    b. wood _____

    c. clear glass _____

    d. waxed paper _____

    e. rocks _____

    f. frosted glass _____

Process Skills
Inferring

Have you noticed that the top portion of some car windshields
are darkened? Why do you think this is done? Write your answer
on a separate sheet of paper.

Name _____ Date _____

Analyze Information

For items 1–3, circle the letter of the correct answer.

1. A compound microscope contains an eyepiece and a(n) _____ lens.

   a. reflective   **b.** translucent   **c.** objective   **d.** opaque

2. At a concert, the stage crew turns on a light with a blue filter. Maria, who is wearing a red dress, is on the stage. What color does the dress appear to be?

   a. red   **b.** blue   **c.** magenta   **d.** black

3. You perceive differences in _____ when your eyes and your brain respond to different wavelengths of light.

   a. colors   **b.** prisms   **c.** transparencies   **d.** lenses

4. Match the invention with its inventor.

   a. space telescope   Spitzer

   b. reflecting telescope   Janssen

   c. refracting telescope   Leeuwenhoek

   d. compound microscope   Newton

   e. simple microscope   Galileo

Problem Solving

5. Suppose you are tired and want to take a nap one afternoon. You decide to cover the windows to block out the light. Would you choose a white sheet or a dark brown towel to block out the light from your windows? Why?

_____

_____

Name _____   Date _____

6. Suppose you are at an optical store. On the counter are two pairs of glasses that have lenses with the shapes shown. One pair of glasses is for your farsighted friend. The other pair is for your nearsighted friend. Look at the drawings of two eyes below. Correctly identify the vision problems on the line below each eye. Then in front of each eye, draw the type of lens that would correct the vision problem shown.

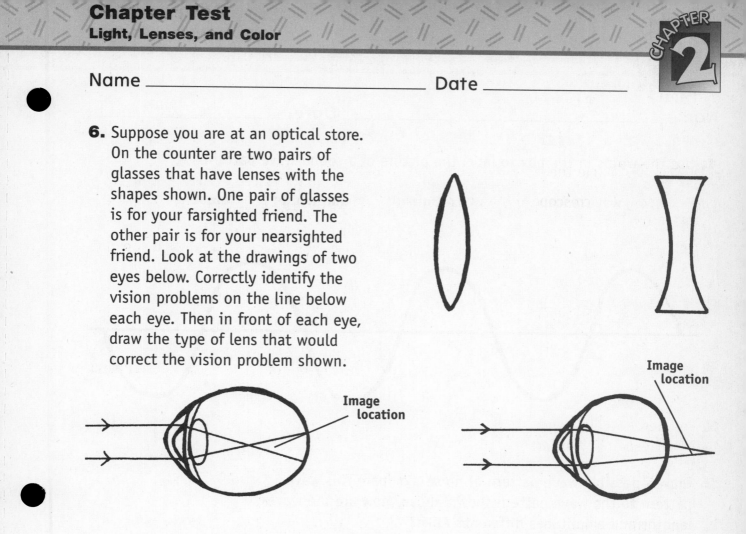

Image location

Image location

_____   _____

Word Power

Use the words in the box to complete each sentence.

convex	focal point	retina	reflecting

Isaac Newton built a _____ telescope that contained a concave mirror and a plane mirror. After striking the mirrors, light passed through a _____ lens, which brought light rays together at the _____ of the lens. This lens helped produce an image on the _____ in the back of the eye.

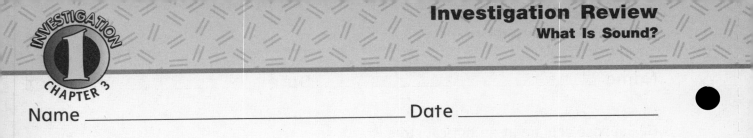

Name _____ Date _____

1. Use the words in the box to label the picture of a sound-wave pattern.

| wavelength | trough | amplitude | crest |

2. Draw a possible wave pattern of noise. Compare this wave pattern to the wave pattern shown above. How are the wavelengths and amplitudes different? Alike?

_____

_____

_____

_____

_____

Process Skills
Making a Hypothesis

How does the sound of a guitar change when the strings are tightened and loosened? How is the frequency of the sound affected by these changes? Write your answer on a separate sheet of paper.

Name _____ Date _____

1. Why can two astronauts on a spacewalk see each other but not hear each other without radios?

_____

_____

2. For each pair of phrases, write which wave travels faster and why.

a. sound in air, sound in steel

_____

_____

b. sound at 15°C, sound at 30°C

_____

_____

_____

_____

Process Skills
Inferring

Suppose you are walking past the gym in your school and you want to know if a game is going on inside. But the door is locked. How does putting your ear to the door help?

_____

_____

_____

Name _____ Date _____

1. Use the clues below to unscramble each word. Write the word
on the line that follows each clue.

   a. ZETHR: Unit used to measure sound frequency _____

   b. VETOCA: Series of eight notes _____

   c. HPTCI: Highness or lowness of sound _____

2. Complete the chart below about the different sounds produced
by musicians in a band.

Musician	Activity	Resulting Sound
singer	shortens vocal cords	Pitch goes _____.
flute player	shortens length of air column	Pitch goes _____.
trumpet player	blows harder	Amplitude _____.
bass guitarist	plays thick, long strings	Pitch goes _____.
keyboard player	plays frequencies of 132 hertz and 264 hertz at the same time	Pitches are 1 _____ apart.

Process Skills
Hypothesizing, Inferring

Suppose you have four identical glass bottles. You fill one bottle
halfway with water and another almost to the top with water.
Then you fill a third bottle halfway with cooking oil and the
fourth almost to the top with oil. Then you blow across the top
of each bottle. How will the sounds differ? How will they be the
same? Explain your answer on a separate sheet of paper.

Name _____ Date _____

Analyze Information

For items 1–3, circle the letter of the correct answer.

1. If someone says "Turn it down!" the person means that you should decrease the sound's ____.

   a. amplitude   **b.** pitch   **c.** overtones   **d.** timbre

2. You are several kilometers from a thunderstorm. Which of the following statements describes the correct sequence of events?

   a. You hear a clap of thunder and then see a flash of lightning.

   b. You see a flash of lightning and then hear a clap of thunder.

   c. You hear thunder and see lightning at the same time.

   d. It is impossible to know without knowing the temperature of the air.

3. Sound travels the fastest through ____.

   a. air on a hot day   **c.** a vacuum

   b. air on a cold day   **d.** a metal bar

Problem Solving

4. Look at the drawing of sound waves below. Explain what happened to the amplitude and frequency of the wave.

_____

_____

Name _____ Date _____

5. You are up high in the stands of a large baseball stadium. You see that the runner has slid into home plate, but the umpire doesn't seem to yell "safe" until almost a second later. Does the umpire have slow reflexes, or is there a scientific explanation for the delay?

_____

_____

_____

_____

_____

_____

6. Wind instruments from all over the world have something in common. What is it?

_____

_____

_____

_____

Word Power

Use the words in the box to complete the sentences.

octaves	frequencies	pitch

The human voice produces sounds in a wide range of _____. In choral groups, high voices may sing a C at 528 hertz. The low voices sing a C at 132 hertz—two _____ lower. Someone with long, thick vocal cords may sing tones at an even lower _____, such as 110 hertz.

Name _____ Date _____

1. Label the sound waves using the words in the box.

| large amplitude | soft sound | small amplitude | loud sound |

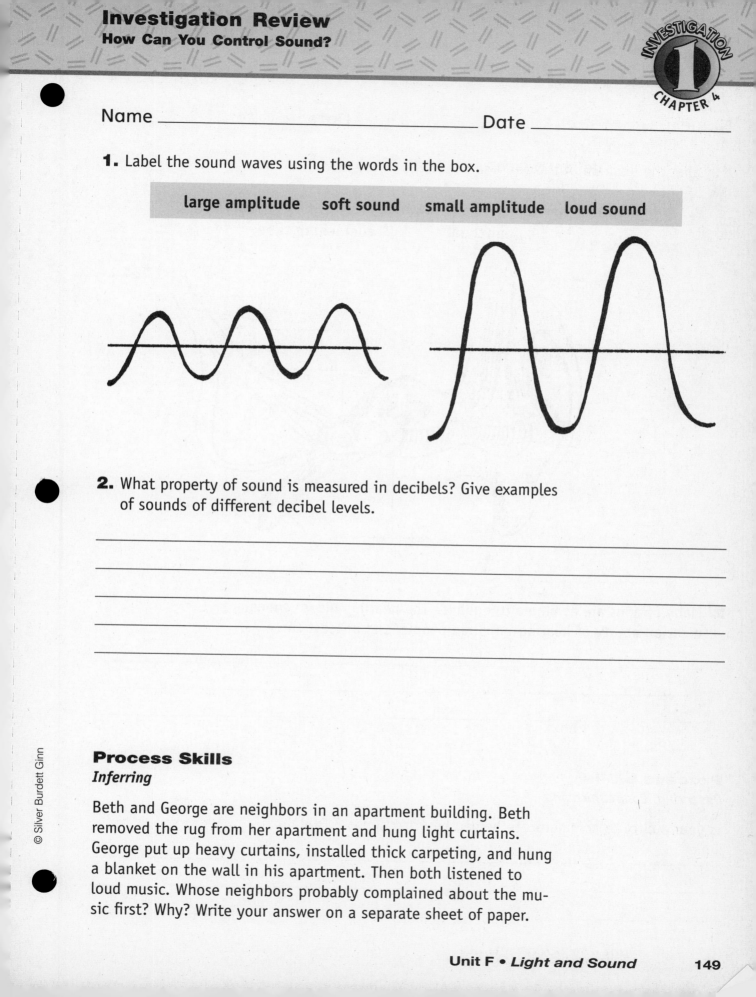

2. What property of sound is measured in decibels? Give examples of sounds of different decibel levels.

_____

_____

_____

_____

_____

Process Skills
Inferring

Beth and George are neighbors in an apartment building. Beth removed the rug from her apartment and hung light curtains. George put up heavy curtains, installed thick carpeting, and hung a blanket on the wall in his apartment. Then both listened to loud music. Whose neighbors probably complained about the music first? Why? Write your answer on a separate sheet of paper.

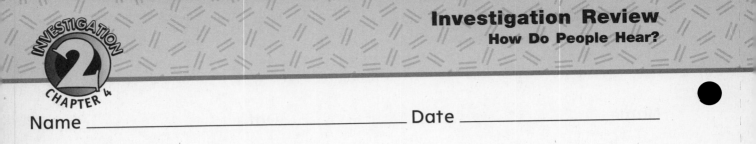
Name _____ Date _____

1. Label the diagram of the ear. Use the words in the box.

auditory nerve	cochlea	eardrum
ear canal	eustachian tube	

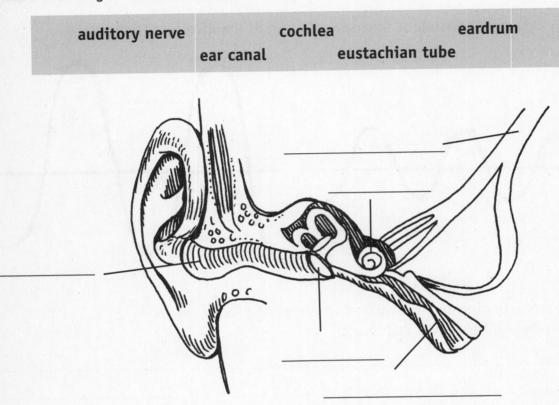

2. Many options are available to enhance the hearing and/or communication ability of hearing-impaired people. List at least three.

_____

_____

_____

Process Skills
Observing, Communicating

Is your ability to communicate helped by other senses? Explain.

_____

_____

_____

Name _____ Date _____

1. Draw a line connecting the recording device on the right to its characteristics on the left.

   a. A laser reads a series of pits and flat areas that represent electric signals.

   phonograph record

   b. The magnetic field of tiny crystals of iron oxide respond to changing electric signals.

   CD

   c. A stylus vibrates as it moves over the tiny hills and valleys of a spiral track.

   audiocassettes

2. Number these items in order from 1 to 5 to show the history of recording sound. 1 = oldest; 5 = newest.

   _____ CDs

   _____ long-playing records

   _____ Edison's phonograph

   _____ Berliner's masters

   _____ audiocassette tape

Process Skills
Inferring

You leave some of your favorite audiocassettes in the science laboratory near a powerful magnet belonging to the teacher. You later find that your tapes are distorted. What happened?

_____

_____

_____

Name _____ Date _____

Analyzing Information

For items 1–3, circle the letter of the correct answer.

1. A stylus and cartridge are parts of which sound device?

a. phonograph

b. audiocassette

c. CD

d. hearing aid

2. Which of the following materials would be the best flooring to use to absorb sound?

a. concrete

c. carpeting

b. tile

d. wood

3. The sound having the highest decibel level is _____.

a. heavy traffic

b. whispering

c. thunder

d. nearby rocket taking off

Problem Solving

4. The information superhighway provides people with many advantages. Describe three advantages of using the information superhighway and one disadvantage of using it.

_____

_____

_____

_____

_____

Name _____ Date _____

5. Why does swallowing when you are in an airplane help to relieve the pressure in your ears?

_____

_____

_____

6. Explain how a hearing aid can help a person with a hearing loss.

_____

_____

_____

_____

_____

Word Power

Fill in the blanks using the words from the box.

compact disc	volume	decibels	auditory nerve

To play a _____, a laser reads pits and flat areas and produces a digital code. The _____ of the sound waves produced from the coded signal is measured in _____. In your ear, vibrations caused by sound waves travel to your _____, and then into your brain. Then you hear your favorite song.

Name _____ Date _____

SOUND IDEAS AT THE SPEED OF LIGHT

Have you ever heard the expression "Now you see it, now you don't"? You and your partner will write riddles or draw pictures to explain some important ideas about sound. Part of the task will be to choose colored markers and cellophane that will "hide" the answers or some part of the picture. When the cellophane is lifted, your message shows in a flash! If you have worked on any musical instruments for the unit project, bring them in for sound effects while you show your cards.

Materials

✔ colored markers
✔ index cards
✔ colored cellophane
✔ tape

Procedure

1. In the Data Space on page 155, answer the questions below. Then you and your partner will make a set of cards with riddles about each question.

　a. How does light travel?

　b. What happens to light when it goes through a lens? Strikes a mirror?

　c. How does sound travel through different materials?

　d. What are the characteristics of musical sounds?

　e. What are some ways that sound is recorded?

After you have written your answers, decide on the color combinations of markers and cellophane you will use for each card. Record them in the Data Space. Remember that you will write some information so that it can be read through the cellophane and some information so that it will be hidden by the cellophane.

Name _____   Date _____

2. With your partner, decide which of you will do each task from the Task List. On the line below, list the task you've chosen. You can ask your partner to help with your task, but you are in charge of completing it. If you choose *Create the art*, include the color combinations that you and your partner chose. Your job will also be to explain what happens when

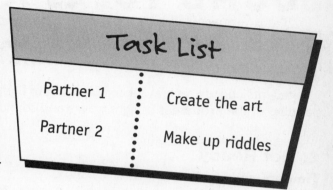

Task List

Partner 1 ⋮ Create the art

Partner 2 ⋮ Make up riddles

different colors of light are mixed. Then tape some cellophane onto five index cards so that the cellophane can be lifted. If you choose *Make up riddles*, create riddles or funny drawings about light and sound that illustrate the answers to the five questions on page 154. For example, you could ask how long it takes before a shark hears the splash of a swimmer 2 km away. You might write the answer and draw the shark in a color that would be hidden by the cellophane.

Task _____

Sound Ideas at the Speed of Light
Data Space

SOUND IDEAS AT THE SPEED OF LIGHT

Students choose several subconcepts about light and sound that show an understanding of the properties of light waves and sound waves.

1. Get Ready

Time: 50 minutes

Grouping: Pairs

Collaborative Strategy: You may wish to suggest that students brainstorm the answers to the questions in groups of four. However, they should work in pairs to complete the tasks. To assess cooperative learning skills, use the Group Skills Checklist provided in this book.

Materials: (each student)
- colored markers
- index cards
- colored cellophane
- tape

2. Guide the Procedure

Explain to students that they are going to make five cards that will allow them to demonstrate what they have learned about light and sound in this unit. Have them read the student pages to themselves and ask questions. Explain that the task can be completed at their work stations, but that you will be available for questions. As students are working, move from group to group, observing performance and answering questions. At the end of the activity, invite students to present their completed cards. Afterward, gather students' worksheets so that they can be scored.

3. Assess the Performance

Use the scoring rubric to help you evaluate students' work.
- Have students created cards that show an understanding of how light and sound travel and how color is filtered?
- Have students communicated through their riddles or diagrams concepts about how sound travels and light is transmitted?

Name _____ Date _____

SOUND IDEAS AT THE SPEED OF LIGHT

Concept: Light and sound travel in waves that have certain identifiable properties.

Assessed items	Points	What to look for
Answers to questions	3	Five answers, based on an understanding of the properties of light waves and sound waves, are clearly indicated and each correctly answers one question.
	2	Five answers are indicated, but two or more do not answer the questions correctly.
	1	The answers to the five questions are unclear or missing.
Task: Create the art	3	The student uses colored cellophane and markers correctly to demonstrate on all five cards what happens when different colors are mixed.
	2	The student uses colored cellophane and markers correctly to demonstrate what happens when different colors are mixed, but two or more cards are incorrect.
	1	The cards and colors are not correctly represented.
Task: Make up riddles	3	The student's riddles, drawings, or diagrams on all five cards accurately demonstrate an understanding of how light and sound travel in waves with specific properties.
	2	The student's riddles, drawings, or diagrams accurately represent the information about light and sound, but two or more cards are incorrect.
	1	The student's riddles, drawings, or diagrams are unclear or missing.

Name _____ Date _____

Analyze Information

For items 1–8, circle the letter of the correct answer.

1. You recognize a voice mainly by its ____.

   a. pitch   **c.** frequency

   b. amplitude   **d.** timbre

Use the graph to answer questions 2–4.

Animal	Range Heard / Range Produced
Dog	
Human	Range Heard / Range Produced
Cat	
Dolphin	
Bat	

| 10 Hz | 100 | 1,000 | 10,000 | 100,000 |

2. Some people use a dog whistle, which humans can't hear, to call their dogs. What can you infer about this whistle?

   a. A dog whistle has a frequency well above 10,000 Hz.

   b. A dog whistle doesn't produce sound.

   c. A dog whistle has a frequency below 100 Hz.

   d. A dog whistle vibrates at 1000 Hz.

3. Humans and bats can both hear which of the same sounds?

   a. a hum at 20 Hz   **c.** noise at 4,000 Hz

   b. a kettle drum at 150 Hz   **d.** a dolphin's call at 100,000 Hz.

Name _____ Date _____

4. Which of the following statements is true?

    a. A cat can produce a greater range of sounds than a dolphin.

    b. All animals shown can hear a greater range of sounds than they can produce.

    c. A bat and a human can produce sounds of the same frequencies.

    d. All animals shown can produce a greater range of frequencies than they can hear.

5. Which of the following is <u>not</u> part of the electromagnetic spectrum?

    a. radio waves   **c.** visible light

    b. microwaves   **d.** audible sound

6. Many devices, from electric light bulbs to battery-operated hearing aids, show that _____.

    a. sound and light waves are the same.

    b. energy can be converted from one kind to another.

    c. sound and light travel at the same speed.

    d. technological advances come slowly.

7. When light passes from air to a glass lens or a glass of water, the light changes _____.

    a. color   **c.** direction

    b. wavelength   **d.** amplitude

8. Lightly plucking a tightened, thin guitar string will produce a sound with a relatively _____.

    a. high decibel level   **c.** high amplitude

    b. low pitch   **d.** high pitch

UNIT
F

Name _____ Date _____

Problem Solving

9. Compare light waves and sound waves. Include at least two properties.

_____

_____

_____

_____

_____

10. Choose one of the following: wind instruments, percussion instruments, the human voice. Explain where the sound is made and how the pitch of the sound can be changed.

_____

_____

_____

_____

_____

_____

11. Suppose you and your friends want to start a band. You decide to practice in your basement because it is a large empty room with a cement floor and walls. What might you do to your basement to reduce the amount of sound throughout the rest of your house when your band is practicing?

_____

_____

_____

_____

12. Suppose your digital watch alarm is broken and you can't turn it off. The sound is really bothering you. Your friend suggests that you wrap the watch in a cloth and put it in a wooden box, but you can still hear the alarm. Why are you still able to hear the sound?

_____

_____

_____

Word Power

Match each term on the left with the correct definition on the right.

13. frequency   number of waves produced each second

14. concave   measure of sound intensity

15. timbre   distance from a point on one wave to the same point on the next wave

16. refraction   bending of light

17. translucent   quality of a sound

18. decibel   lens that is thicker at the edges than at the center

19. reflection   allowing some light to pass through it

20. wavelength   bouncing of light from a surface

CHAPTER 1

Name _____ Date _____

1. The terms in the box are different kinds of joints. Match each part of the body in the drawing with the kind of joint that helps it move.

> **ball-and-socket joint**
> **hinge joint**
> **pivot joint**
> **gliding joint**

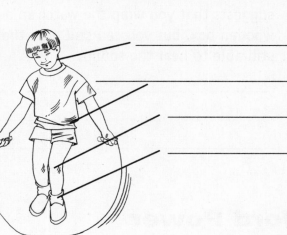

_____
_____
_____
_____

2. Use the clues below to unscramble each word. Then use the circled letters to find the answer to the riddle below.

a. Strong bands of fiber that hold bones in place and allow some movement:
M E A T L I N G S   __ __ __ __ __ __Ⓞ__ __

b. Places where bones come together but allow no movement:
B A M O L I V E M   T I N J O S

__ __ __ __ __ __ __ __ __Ⓞ__ __ __ __ __

c. Tissue that is similar to bone but is more flexible:
G I L R A T A C E   __ __ __ __Ⓞ__ __ __ __

d. What the ribs do for the heart, lungs, and soft organs:
R E T T O C P   __ __Ⓞ__ __ __ __

e. The middle part of a long bone: T H A F S   __ __ __ __Ⓞ

Riddle: Where is the favorite place for bones to meet each other?_____

Process Skills
Making and Using Models

Suppose you want to make a model of the bones and immovable joints in the skull. You have a plastic-foam ball and some modeling clay to work with. On a separate sheet of paper, draw or write how you would show how the bones of the skull protect the brain.

Name _____ Date _____

1. Use the words in the box to complete the sentences in the paragraph below.

arm	**bend**	**biceps**
relaxes	**pairs**	**triceps**

Skeletal muscles work in _____ to move parts of your body. The _____ and triceps in your arm work like a team. When the biceps contracts, the _____ muscle stretches and relaxes. These movements make your arm _____ at the elbow. When the triceps contracts, the other muscle of the pair _____. That straightens your _____.

2. Write the missing words.

kinds of muscle

a. _____ muscles move bones.

b. _____ muscles are found in the stomach.

c. _____ muscles make up the heart.

muscle injuries

d. A _____ is a "charley horse."

e. A _____ is an overstretched muscle.

f. A _____ is a torn ligament.

Process Skills
Communicating

Suppose you joined a bicycle club that will be riding long distances. What precautions can you take to prepare for these rides? What can you do to avoid injury? Write your answer on a separate sheet of paper.

Name _____ Date _____

Analyze Information

1. The pictures show how paired muscles work to bend and straighten your arms. What happens to the biceps and triceps muscles when the girl bends her elbow? Express your answer by labeling the arm muscles in the second diagram.

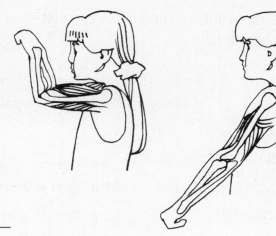

2. What are the three main functions of the skeletal system?

_____

_____

_____

_____

_____

Problem Solving

3. This is a closeup view of what it looks like inside the shoulder joint. Draw arrow(s) to show where the ligaments are.

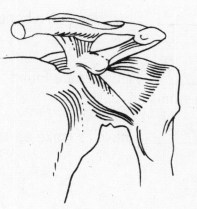

4. How do the bones, ligaments, and cartilage of the shoulder joint shown work together?

_____

_____

_____

_____

5. How could you use clay and wire to model your ribs? What is the function of the ribs? Write or draw your answer on a separate sheet of paper.

Name _____ Date _____

6. Sometimes people have an injury or a disease that makes the movement of the hip joint painful or impossible. The joint is removed and replaced with metal and/or plastic parts. In the space below, draw the shape of a hip replacement joint that would enable a person to walk again.

Word Power

Circle the letter that correctly answers each question.

7. Which kind of muscle helps move food through your digestive system?

a. skeletal muscle   **c.** cardiac muscle

b. smooth muscle   **d.** triceps muscle

8. You jump up to get a basketball rebound. You come down hard and your foot is twisted. Ouch! You fall to the gym floor in pain. What is the likely diagnosis for your ankle?

a. sprain   **b.** strain   **d.** fracture   **c.** dislocation

9. What structure in your neck allows you to look back and forth?

a. bone   **c.** joint

b. ligament   **d.** tendon

10. Blood cells are made in the marrow of what structures?

a. bones   **b.** joints   **c.** cartilage   **d.** cardiac muscles

Name _____ Date _____

1. Draw a line to match each part of the nervous system with the job that it does.

a. motor neurons   receive stimuli from the environment

b. medulla   part of the brain that controls heartbeat rate

c. spinal cord   path that nerve impulses travel to and from the brain

d. sensory neurons   travels at 120 meters per second

e. nerve impulse   part of the brain that controls muscles and coordination

f. cerebrum   give signals for muscles to respond

g. cerebellum   part of the brain related to thinking and emotions

2. For each example, write *sensory* or *motor* for the type of neuron that would carry the message through your body.

a. You hear your favorite song. _____

b. You start dancing. _____

c. You step on your bike pedal. _____

d. You smell something burning. _____

e. You pull socks out of a drawer. _____

Process Skills
Predicting

Joe is learning to drive a car. During his third drive, a dog steps into the road. It takes Joe two seconds to step on the brake. How much time would it take him to respond to the same thing after he had been driving several months? Why?

_____

_____

Investigation Review
How Can You Respond to Things Around You?

INVESTIGATION
2
CHAPTER 2

Name _____ Date _____

1. Give an example of how the students in the picture experience each of the five senses.

_____

_____

_____

_____

2. Write the stage of mental development described in each situation.

a. Lucy can find her way home from school. She can draw a map of her neighborhood, and she understands the concepts of time and geography. Lucy is in _____.

b. Jessie is asking "Why?" all the time. She can now use language to talk and think about the past and future. Though she is learning to share, it is difficult because she thinks the world revolves around her. Jessie is in

_____.

c. Brendan's brain has already been growing for nine months. His mind is very active and it will continue to grow much more. Brendan is in the _____ stage of development.

d. Claire can solve complex problems by forming a hypothesis and testing the hypothesis in a logical way. She also often thinks about her own thoughts and life as she discovers more about herself. Claire is in _____.

Process Skills
Predicting

Suppose someone throws a snowball toward your face. How would you respond? Is your response voluntary or automatic? Write your answer on a separate sheet of paper.

Name _____ Date _____

Analyze Information

1. Ronnie just went into a pizza parlor for a pizza. She can already smell the wonderful aroma. What is the stimulus that allows her to smell the pizza? What receptors receive the stimulus?

_____

2. Where do the nerve impulses relaying the pizza odor have to go for Ronnie to recognize that she is smelling pizza?

_____

_____

_____

3. Ronnie has many small receptors on her tongue like the one shown. What are they? What sense are these receptors part of? What different stimuli do these receptors respond to?

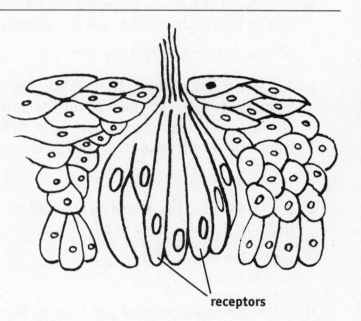

receptors

_____

_____

_____

_____

Problem Solving

4. A computer program can measure reaction time. When Carlos hears a tone or sees a picture, he hits "Enter" on his keyboard. The computer measures the reaction time in thousandths of a second. What is the stimulus and response in this example?

_____

_____

Name _____ Date _____

5. Have you ever played a guessing game where you
blindfold a person and he or she identifies items in a
bag by feeling them? Why is this possible?

_____

_____

_____

_____

6. How well do you think you would be able to taste if you lost
your sense of smell? Can you think of a time when this might
happen temporarily?

_____

_____

_____

_____

Word Power

Circle the letter of each correct answer.

7. Barry is thinking about a wish list for his birthday. He is using his ____ .

   a. cerebellum   **b.** cerebrum   **c.** medulla   **d.** sensory cortex

8. A response that helps you protect your body is probably a ____ .

   a. heartbeat   **b.** brain wave pattern   **c.** motor neuron   **d.** reflex

9. Information about sound vibrations is carried by nerve impulses along the ____ .

   a. optic nerve   **b.** auditory nerve   **c.** spinal cord   **d.** retina

10. ____ are signals that start a nerve impulse.

   a. motor neurons   **c.** auditory nerves

   b. stimuli   **d.** brain waves

Name _____ Date _____

1. Match each term with its definition.

a. addiction

drug found in coffee, chocolate, some teas, and some soft drinks

b. nicotine

a group of drugs that can be legally purchased without a prescription

c. caffeine

stimulant found in tobacco

d. steroids

drugs that severely depress the nervous system and can cause death from overdose

e. narcotics

drugs that act like the body's natural hormones

f. over-the-counter drugs

dependency on a substance that makes it difficult to stop using it

2. Write each of the drugs listed in the correct column. Star the drugs that are illegal.

alcohol	cocaine	marijuana
amphetamines	heroin	nicotine
crack	LSD	tranquilizers

Stimulants	Depressants	Hallucinogens	Narcotics

Process Skills
Communicating

Some paints, glues, office products, and cleansers contain toxins that can be harmful if inhaled. A single use of any of these substances can cause liver, kidney, or brain damage. On a separate sheet of paper, design an advertisement about the dangers of inhalants.

© Silver Burdett Ginn

Name _____ Date _____

1. Fill in the blanks using the terms in the box.

misused	deformed	heat	liver damage
blood system	depresses	judgment	mental illness

Some people may drink alcohol to relax, but alcohol can be dangerous when it

is _____. Unlike food, alcohol is absorbed by the

_____ quickly. Alcohol causes _____ loss, which

makes the drinker feel colder. Alcohol also _____ the nervous sys-

tem, causing people to become slow and clumsy. Abused over a long time, alcohol

can cause _____, _____, and heart disease. Sadly,

if a pregnant woman drinks, her unborn child could be born _____

or with severe damage to the nervous system. Alcohol impairs _____,

and a person who drives while drinking can cause accidents.

2. Fill in the chart with the effects alcohol has on the human body.

Short-Term Effects	Long-Term Effects

Process Skills
Communicating, Making Decisions

You have just watched a sporting event on television and seen
commercials for alcoholic beverages. You've decided to write a
letter to the television network about the ads. On a separate
sheet of paper list the main points you will make in your letter.

© Silver Burdett Ginn

Name _____ Date _____

Analyze Information

For questions 1–4, circle the letter of the best answer.

1. Which of the following substances is absorbed directly into the bloodstream, depresses the nervous system, and causes long-term liver and heart disease?

  a. nicotine

  b. any drug

  c. alcohol

  d. caffeine

2. Which of the following is a fatal disease of the body's immune system that can be spread by improper use of needles?

  a. alcoholism

  b. AIDS

  c. addiction

  d. cancer

3. Drugs that act like hormones and can damage the heart and other organs are ____.

  a. stimulants

  b. narcotics

  c. inhalants

  d. steroids

4. Marijuana, hashish, and LSD are all kinds of ____, which can alter perception and awareness.

  a. stimulants

  b. hallucinogens

  c. depressants

  d. narcotics

© Silver Burdett Ginn

Name _____ Date _____

Problem Solving

5. Suppose you are at a friend's house and her older brother asks you to try some illegal drugs. What should you do?

_____

_____

_____

_____

6. Suppose you find out that a friend is using stimulants to be more alert and active at sports. What could you tell your friend to discourage her from using these drugs?

_____

_____

_____

_____

Word Power

Fill in each blank with a word or phrase from the box.

stimulants	narcotics	hallucinogens	depressants

7. barbiturates, tranquilizers, alcohol _____

8. morphine, heroin _____

9. nicotine, amphetamines, cocaine, crack _____

10. marijuana, LSD _____

Name _____ Date _____

READY, SET, CONCENTRATE!

. . . .

You and your partner will create a card game using drawings of the parts of the human body that you studied in this unit. As you play the game, you will measure your partner's "learning curve" by timing how long it takes your partner to make the correct matches.

Materials

✔ index cards
✔ markers
✔ timer

Procedure

1. With your partner, list ten parts of the body discussed in this unit—five parts from the nervous system (The Brain) and five parts from the skeletal and muscular systems (The Frame). Include a description of each part and how it works. Write your list in the Data Space and, if necessary, on a separate sheet of paper.

Data Space

Name _____ Date _____

2. Choose a task. One partner should *Be the Brain*. The other should *Build the Frame*. Then each player takes a stack of ten blank cards, two cards for each body part listed for their task in the Data Space. On the first card of each pair, write the name of the body part and make a drawing of the part. On the second card, describe the part, tell how it works, and explain how it is affected by drugs and alcohol.

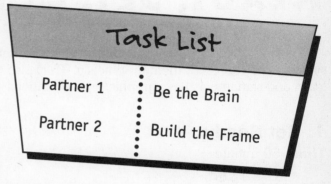

Task List

Partner 1 ⋮ Be the Brain

Partner 2 ⋮ Build the Frame

3. Play the game. Shuffle your deck of ten cards and spread them face down for your partner. Say "Ready, set, concentrate!" and set the timer. Your partner must turn over two cards at random. If the cards do not match, the player puts them face down again and tries two more cards. When there is a match, note the time and write it down. When all the cards are matched, the sum of the five times listed will be that player's score.

Now reverse roles. Your partner should shuffle and spread the other deck of ten cards and time you as you make matches. Continue the play until both players have had three chances to play. Then compare your times.

4. Play the game with all twenty cards. Spread all the cards face down. Take turns turning over two cards at a time. When you make a match, remove the cards and go again. The player with the most cards when play ends wins.

© Silver Burdett Ginn

READY, SET, CONCENTRATE!

Students choose several structures of the skeletal, muscular, and nervous systems and represent them graphically. They also test one another's ability to learn and remember these graphic representations over several trials.

1. Get Ready

Time: 50 minutes

Grouping: Pairs

Collaborative Strategy: You may wish to suggest that students work in groups of four, with two students working on each task. To assess cooperative learning skills, use the Group Skills Checklist provided in this book.

Materials: (each pair of students)
- index cards
- markers
- timer

2. Guide the Procedure

Place the materials needed for the task at each station, and identify student pairs. Explain to students that they are going to complete a task that will allow them to demonstrate what they have learned about the skeletal, muscular, and nervous systems. Explain that they will test one another's ability to learn and remember information over several trials.

As students are working, move from group to group, observing performance and answering questions. At the end of the activity, invite students to share the game cards they have made. Afterwards, gather students' cards and time reports so that they can be scored.

3. Assess Performance

Use the scoring rubric to help you evaluate students' work.
- Have students used good decision-making skills in choosing structures of the human body systems and in describing their functions?
- Have students created cards that show an understanding of how the structures of the human body systems function? Have they explained how drugs affect these systems?

Name _____ Date _____

READY, SET, CONCENTRATE!
···

Concept: The structures of skeletal, muscular, and nervous systems work together to support and control life functions. Coordination of the senses, the nerves, and the brain make learning and memory possible. Drugs affect the human body systems in different ways.

Assessed items	Points	What to look for
Choice of body system parts, descriptions, and affect of drugs on systems	3	The ten parts chosen from each system, their description, and how drugs affect these systems, are clearly indicated.
	2	The parts of each system, their descriptions, and how drugs affect these systems are somewhat clearly indicated.
	1	The parts of each system, their descriptions, and how drugs affect these systems are unclear or missing.
Task Option 1: Build the Frame—making ten Skeletal and Muscular Systems cards and completing time reports	3	The *Build the Frame* student draws ten cards accurately and makes a time report that reflects the partner's performance.
	2	Ten cards were drawn, but half or more show inaccurate information and/or the time report is not clear.
	1	Fewer than three cards were made, and the information is inaccurate or not given and/or the time report was not made.
Task Option 2: Be the Brain—making ten Nervous System cards and completing time reports	3	The *Be the Brain* student draws ten cards accurately and makes a time report that reflects the partner's performance.
	2	Ten cards were drawn, but half or more show inaccurate information and/or the time report is not clear.
	1	Fewer than three cards were made, and the information is inaccurate or not given and/or the time report was not made.

Name _____ Date _____

Analyze Information

1. Label each part of this bone and describe its function.

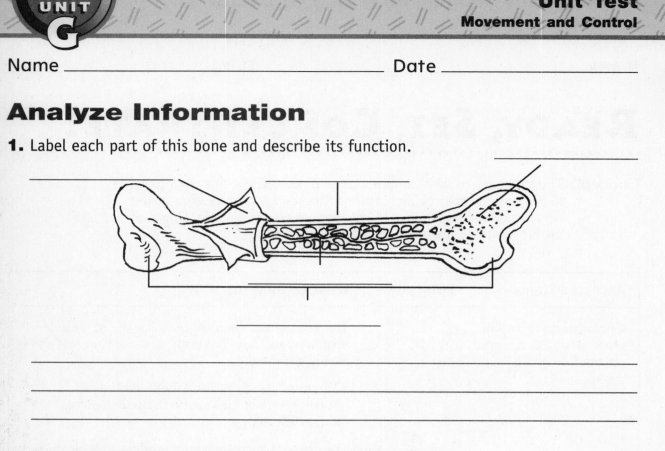

_____

_____

_____

2. The round end of the femur fits into a depression in the hip
bone. What is that kind of meeting place called?

_____

3. Nerve impulses travel from receptors in your nose to the brain.
The brain then interprets these impulses, using its memory
bank, and odors are identified. Write which sense is described. _____

4. This chart shows some of the effects of alcohol on the brain.
Fill in the columns with the part of the brain that controls
each function.

Effect	Part of the Brain
Loss of judgment and impaired mental abilities	
Loss of balance and coordination	
Reflexes slow down	

Name _____ Date _____

Use the picture below to answer questions 5–8.

5. Label the stimulus, the sensory
neurons, and the motor neurons
in the picture.

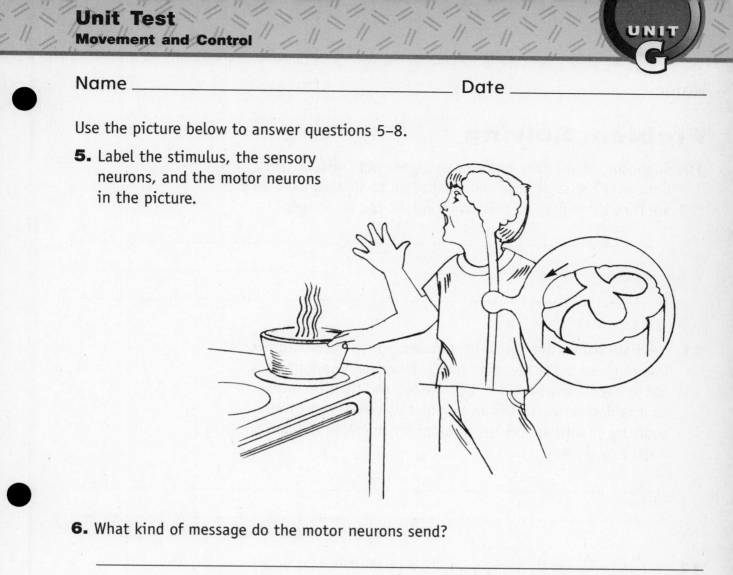

6. What kind of message do the motor neurons send?

_____

_____

7. What pathway carries this impulse to the brain? When will the
person know what has happened?

_____

_____

8. Which sense receptors are receiving stimuli?

_____

9. Kyle's dog sees Kyle throw a ball. The dog sees the ball, leaps,
and snatches the ball in midair. What could you call the time
it takes the dog to respond?

_____

Name _____ Date _____

Problem Solving

10. Suppose you are baby-sitting two 2-year-old children. They fight over the same toys and can't seem to share things. Why are they behaving like this? What might you do to help?

_____

_____

_____

11. Newborn babies are born with reflexes, which they outgrow. One of these is the stepping reflex. When held upright on a flat surface a newborn may lift one leg and then the other, as if taking steps. This is an involuntary reflex that disappears by about two months in order for the child to learn to walk. Explain why.

_____

_____

12. You and your family enjoy going to a restaurant near your home, but it doesn't have a nonsmoking section. On a separate sheet of paper, write a letter stating the arguments you would use to convince the owners to make a nonsmoking section.

13. The breath tester shows the results of a blood alcohol test given to a driver. Is the driver in trouble? Why or why not? Why are laws needed to regulate this problem?

_____

_____

_____

_____

Name _____ Date _____

14. Suppose your school is having a Drug Awareness Week. What would you write on a poster to make others aware of the dangers of taking drugs?

_____

_____

Word Power

Circle the letter of the word or words to complete each sentence.

15. Bones are joined to bones by _____.

a. cartilage   c. ligaments

b. tendons   d. periosteum

16. Muscles damaged in a heart attack are _____ muscles.

a. cardiac   c. skeletal

b. smooth   d. biceps

17. Heat, cold, pressure, and pain are stimuli sensed by _____.

a. light receptors   c. touch receptors

b. auditory receptors   d. smell receptors

18. Sounds are vibrations that travel through the ear canal and eardrum to the inner ear, where they become nerve impulses moving to the brain along the _____.

a. auditory nerve   c. optic nerve

b. brainwaves   d. taste buds

19. Nicotine and caffeine are commonly used _____.

a. depressants   c. narcotics

b. stimulants   d. steroids

20. A substance that is difficult to stop using is said to be _____.

a. an over-the-counter drug   c. a prescription drug

b. addictive   d. a steroid

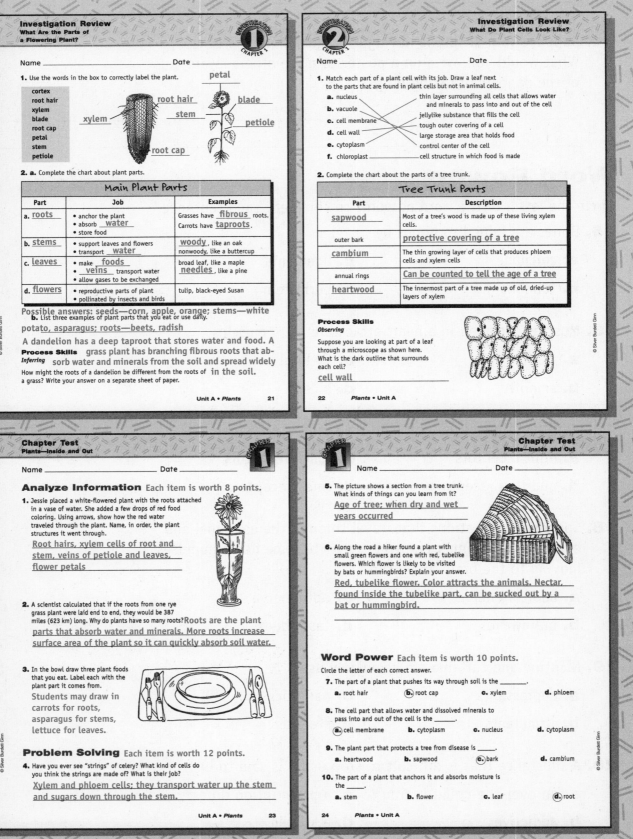

Investigation Review (CHAPTER 1 — INVESTIGATION 1)
What Are the Parts of a Flowering Plant?

Name _____ Date _____

1. Use the words in the box to correctly label the plant.

Box: cortex, root hair, xylem, blade, root cap, petal, stem, petiole

Labels: root hair, xylem, root cap — petal, blade, stem, petiole

2. a. Complete the chart about plant parts.

Main Plant Parts

Part	Job	Examples
a. **roots**	• anchor the plant • absorb **water** • store food	Grasses have **fibrous** roots. Carrots have **taproots**.
b. **stems**	• support leaves and flowers • transport **water**	**woody**, like an oak nonwoody, like a buttercup
c. **leaves**	• make **foods** **veins** transport water • allow gases to be exchanged	broad leaf, like a maple **needles**, like a pine
d. **flowers**	• reproductive parts of plant • pollinated by insects and birds	tulip, black-eyed Susan

b. List three examples of plant parts that you eat or use daily.

Possible answers: seeds—corn, apple, orange; stems—white potato, asparagus; roots—beets, radish

Process Skills
Inferring
How might the roots of a dandelion be different from the roots of a grass? Write your answer on a separate sheet of paper.

A dandelion has a deep taproot that stores water and food. A grass plant has branching fibrous roots that absorb water and minerals from the soil and spread widely in the soil.

Unit A • *Plants* 21

Investigation Review (CHAPTER 1 — INVESTIGATION 2)
What Do Plant Cells Look Like?

Name _____ Date _____

1. Match each part of a plant cell with its job. Draw a leaf next to the parts that are found in plant cells but not in animal cells.

a. nucleus — thin layer surrounding all cells that allows water and minerals to pass into and out of the cell
b. vacuole — jellylike substance that fills the cell
c. cell membrane — tough outer covering of a cell
d. cell wall — large storage area that holds food
e. cytoplasm — control center of the cell
f. chloroplast — cell structure in which food is made

2. Complete the chart about the parts of a tree trunk.

Tree Trunk Parts

Part	Description
sapwood	Most of a tree's wood is made up of these living xylem cells.
outer bark	**protective covering of a tree**
cambium	The thin growing layer of cells that produces phloem cells and xylem cells
annual rings	**Can be counted to tell the age of a tree**
heartwood	The innermost part of a tree made up of old, dried-up layers of xylem

Process Skills
Observing
Suppose you are looking at part of a leaf through a microscope as shown here. What is the dark outline that surrounds each cell?

cell wall

22 *Plants* • Unit A

Chapter Test (CHAPTER 1)
Plants—Inside and Out

Name _____ Date _____

Analyze Information Each item is worth 8 points.

1. Jessie placed a white-flowered plant with the roots attached in a vase of water. She added a few drops of red food coloring. Using arrows, show how the red water traveled through the plant. Name, in order, the plant structures it went through.

Root hairs, xylem cells of root and stem, veins of petiole and leaves, flower petals

2. A scientist calculated that if the roots from one rye grass plant were laid end to end, they would be 387 miles (623 km) long. Why do plants have so many roots? Roots are the plant parts that absorb water and minerals. More roots increase surface area of the plant so it can quickly absorb soil water.

3. In the bowl draw three plant foods that you eat. Label each with the plant part it comes from.

Students may draw in carrots for roots, asparagus for stems, lettuce for leaves.

Problem Solving Each item is worth 12 points.

4. Have you ever see "strings" of celery? What kind of cells do you think the strings are made of? What is their job?

Xylem and phloem cells; they transport water up the stem and sugars down through the stem.

Unit A • *Plants* 23

Chapter Test (CHAPTER 1)
Plants—Inside and Out

Name _____ Date _____

5. The picture shows a section from a tree trunk. What kinds of things can you learn from it?

Age of tree; when dry and wet years occurred

6. Along the road a hiker found a plant with small green flowers and one with red, tubelike flowers. Which flower is likely to be visited by bats or hummingbirds? Explain your answer.

Red, tubelike flower. Color attracts the animals. Nectar, found inside the tubelike part, can be sucked out by a bat or hummingbird.

Word Power Each item is worth 10 points.

Circle the letter of each correct answer.

7. The part of a plant that pushes its way through soil is the _____.
a. root hair   **b. root cap**   c. xylem   d. phloem

8. The cell part that allows water and dissolved minerals to pass into and out of the cell is the _____.
a. cell membrane   b. cytoplasm   c. nucleus   d. cytoplasm

9. The plant part that protects a tree from disease is _____.
a. heartwood   b. sapwood   **c. bark**   d. cambium

10. The part of a plant that anchors it and absorbs moisture is the _____.
a. stem   b. flower   c. leaf   **d. root**

24 *Plants* • Unit A

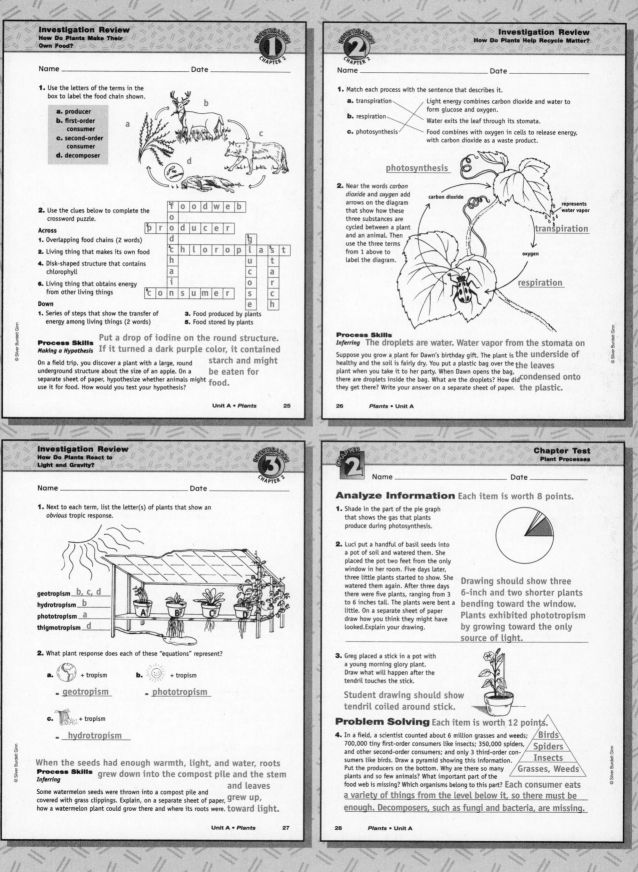

Answers

Investigation Review
How Do Plants Make Their Own Food?

INVESTIGATION 1 CHAPTER 2

Name _____ Date _____

1. Use the letters of the terms in the box to label the food chain shown.

   a. producer
   b. first-order consumer
   c. second-order consumer
   d. decomposer

2. Use the clues below to complete the crossword puzzle.

Across

1. Overlapping food chains (2 words)
2. Living thing that makes its own food
4. Disk-shaped structure that contains chlorophyll
6. Living thing that obtains energy from other living things

Down

1. Series of steps that show the transfer of energy among living things (2 words)
3. Food produced by plants
5. Food stored by plants

Crossword answers: **foodweb**, **producer**, **chloroplast**, **consumer**

Process Skills
Making a Hypothesis

On a field trip, you discover a plant with a large, round underground structure about the size of an apple. On a separate sheet of paper, hypothesize whether animals might use it for food. How would you test your hypothesis?

Put a drop of iodine on the round structure. If it turned a dark purple color, it contained starch and might be eaten for food.

Unit A • Plants   25

Investigation Review
How Do Plants Help Recycle Matter?

INVESTIGATION 2 CHAPTER 2

Name _____ Date _____

1. Match each process with the sentence that describes it.

   a. transpiration — Light energy combines carbon dioxide and water to form glucose and oxygen.
   b. respiration — Water exits the leaf through its stomata.
   c. photosynthesis — Food combines with oxygen in cells to release energy, with carbon dioxide as a waste product.

2. Near the words *carbon dioxide* and *oxygen* add arrows on the diagram that show how these three substances are cycled between a plant and an animal. Then use the three terms from 1 above to label the diagram.

photosynthesis · carbon dioxide · represents water vapor · transpiration · oxygen · respiration

Process Skills
Inferring

Suppose you grow a plant for Dawn's birthday gift. The plant is healthy and the soil is fairly dry. You put a plastic bag over the plant when you take it to her party. When Dawn opens the bag, there are droplets inside the bag. What are the droplets? How did they get there? Write your answer on a separate sheet of paper.

The droplets are water. Water vapor from the stomata on the underside of the leaves condensed onto the plastic.

26   Plants • Unit A

Investigation Review
How Do Plants React to Light and Gravity?

INVESTIGATION 3 CHAPTER 2

Name _____ Date _____

1. Next to each term, list the letter(s) of plants that show an *obvious* tropic response.

   geotropism __b, c, d__
   hydrotropism __b__
   phototropism __a__
   thigmotropism __d__

2. What plant response does each of these "equations" represent?

   a. 🌍 + tropism = __geotropism__
   b. ☀ + tropism = __phototropism__
   c. 💧 + tropism = __hydrotropism__

Process Skills
Inferring

Some watermelon seeds were thrown into a compost pile and covered with grass clippings. Explain, on a separate sheet of paper, how a watermelon plant could grow there and where its roots were.

When the seeds had enough warmth, light, and water, roots grew down into the compost pile and the stem and leaves grew up, toward light.

Unit A • Plants   27

Chapter Test
Plant Processes

CHAPTER 2

Name _____ Date _____

Analyze Information Each item is worth 8 points.

1. Shade in the part of the pie graph that shows the gas that plants produce during photosynthesis.

2. Luci put a handful of basil seeds into a pot of soil and watered them. She placed the pot two feet from the only window in her room. Five days later, three little plants started to show. She watered them again. After three days there were five plants, ranging from 3 to 6 inches tall. The plants were bent a little. On a separate sheet of paper draw how you think they might have looked. Explain your drawing.

Drawing should show three 6-inch and two shorter plants bending toward the window. Plants exhibited phototropism by growing toward the only source of light.

3. Greg placed a stick in a pot with a young morning glory plant. Draw what will happen after the tendril touches the stick.

Student drawing should show tendril coiled around stick.

Problem Solving Each item is worth 12 points.

4. In a field, a scientist counted about 6 million grasses and weeds; 700,000 tiny first-order consumers like insects; 350,000 spiders; and other second-order consumers; and only 3 third-order consumers like birds. Draw a pyramid showing this information. Put the producers on the bottom. Why are there so many plants and so few animals? What important part of the food web is missing? Which organisms belong to this part?

Pyramid: Birds / Spiders / Insects / Grasses, Weeds

Each consumer eats a variety of things from the level below it, so there must be enough. Decomposers, such as fungi and bacteria, are missing.

28   Plants • Unit A

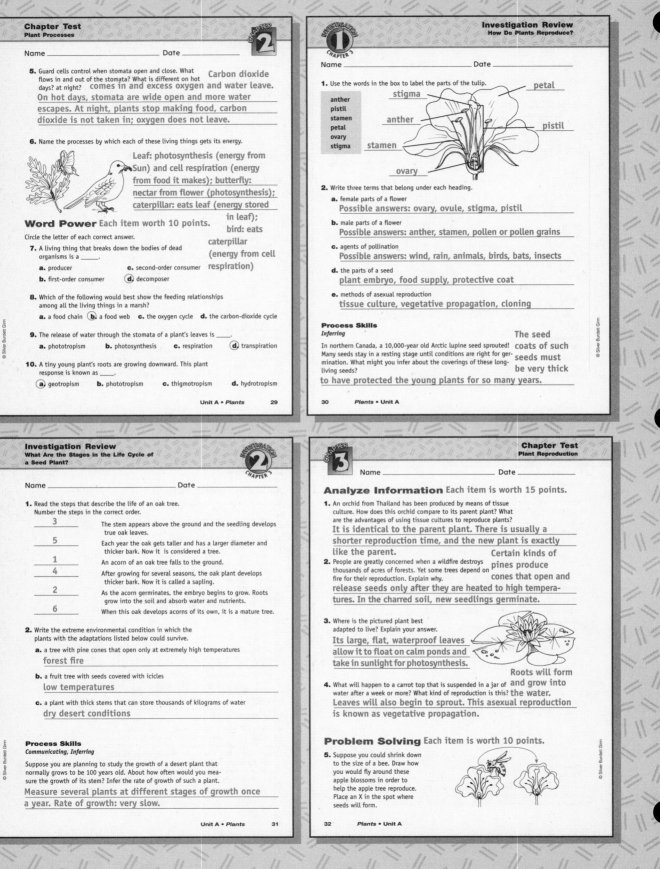

Chapter Test
Plant Processes

CHAPTER 2

Name _____ Date _____

5. Guard cells control when stomata open and close. What flows in and out of the stomata? What is different on hot days? at night? **Carbon dioxide comes in and excess oxygen and water leave.** On hot days, stomata are wide open and more water escapes. At night, plants stop making food, carbon dioxide is not taken in; oxygen does not leave.

6. Name the processes by which each of these living things gets its energy.

Leaf: photosynthesis (energy from Sun) and cell respiration (energy from food it makes); butterfly: nectar from flower (photosynthesis); caterpillar: eats leaf (energy stored in leaf); bird: eats caterpillar (energy from cell respiration)

Word Power Each item worth 10 points.

Circle the letter of each correct answer.

7. A living thing that breaks down the bodies of dead organisms is a _____.
   a. producer   c. second-order consumer
   b. first-order consumer   **d. decomposer**

8. Which of the following would best show the feeding relationships among all the living things in a marsh?
   a. a food chain   **b. a food web**   c. the oxygen cycle   d. the carbon-dioxide cycle

9. The release of water through the stomata of a plant's leaves is _____.
   a. phototropism   b. photosynthesis   c. respiration   **d. transpiration**

10. A tiny young plant's roots are growing downward. This plant response is known as _____.
    a. geotropism   b. phototropism   c. thigmotropism   d. hydrotropism

Unit A • Plants   29

Investigation Review
How Do Plants Reproduce?

INVESTIGATION 1 CHAPTER 3

Name _____ Date _____

1. Use the words in the box to label the parts of the tulip.

anther
pistil
stamen
petal
ovary
stigma

stigma — anther — stamen — ovary — petal — pistil

2. Write three terms that belong under each heading.
   a. female parts of a flower
      Possible answers: ovary, ovule, stigma, pistil
   b. male parts of a flower
      Possible answers: anther, stamen, pollen or pollen grains
   c. agents of pollination
      Possible answers: wind, rain, animals, birds, bats, insects
   d. the parts of a seed
      plant embryo, food supply, protective coat
   e. methods of asexual reproduction
      tissue culture, vegetative propagation, cloning

Process Skills
Inferring

In northern Canada, a 10,000-year old Arctic lupine seed sprouted! Many seeds stay in a resting stage until conditions are right for germination. What might you infer about the coverings of these long-living seeds? **The seed coats of such seeds must be very thick to have protected the young plants for so many years.**

30   Plants • Unit A

Investigation Review
What Are the Stages in the Life Cycle of a Seed Plant?

INVESTIGATION 2 CHAPTER 3

Name _____ Date _____

1. Read the steps that describe the life of an oak tree. Number the steps in the correct order.

   3 The stem appears above the ground and the seedling develops true oak leaves.

   5 Each year the oak gets taller and has a larger diameter and thicker bark. Now it is considered a tree.

   1 An acorn of an oak tree falls to the ground.

   4 After growing for several seasons, the oak plant develops thicker bark. Now it is called a sapling.

   2 As the acorn germinates, the embryo begins to grow. Roots grow into the soil and absorb water and nutrients.

   6 When this oak develops acorns of its own, it is a mature tree.

2. Write the extreme environmental condition in which the plants with the adaptations listed below could survive.
   a. a tree with pine cones that open only at extremely high temperatures
      forest fire
   b. a fruit tree with seeds covered with icicles
      low temperatures
   c. a plant with thick stems that can store thousands of kilograms of water
      dry desert conditions

Process Skills
Communicating, Inferring

Suppose you are planning to study the growth of a desert plant that normally grows to be 100 years old. About how often would you measure the growth of its stem? Infer the rate of growth of such a plant.

Measure several plants at different stages of growth once a year. Rate of growth: very slow.

Unit A • Plants   31

Chapter Test
Plant Reproduction

CHAPTER 3

Name _____ Date _____

Analyze Information Each item is worth 15 points.

1. An orchid from Thailand has been produced by means of tissue culture. How does this orchid compare to its parent plant? What are the advantages of using tissue cultures to reproduce plants? **It is identical to the parent plant. There is usually a shorter reproduction time, and the new plant is exactly like the parent.**

2. People are greatly concerned when a wildfire destroys thousands of acres of forests. Yet some trees depend on fire for their reproduction. Explain why. **Certain kinds of pines produce cones that open and release seeds only after they are heated to high temperatures. In the charred soil, new seedlings germinate.**

3. Where is the pictured plant best adapted to live? Explain your answer. **Its large, flat, waterproof leaves allow it to float on calm ponds and take in sunlight for photosynthesis.**

4. What will happen to a carrot top that is suspended in a jar of water after a week or more? What kind of reproduction is this? **Roots will form and grow into the water. Leaves will also begin to sprout. This asexual reproduction is known as vegetative propagation.**

Problem Solving Each item is worth 10 points.

5. Suppose you could shrink down to the size of a bee. Draw how you would fly around these apple blossoms in order to help the apple tree reproduce. Place an X in the spot where seeds will form.

32   Plants • Unit A

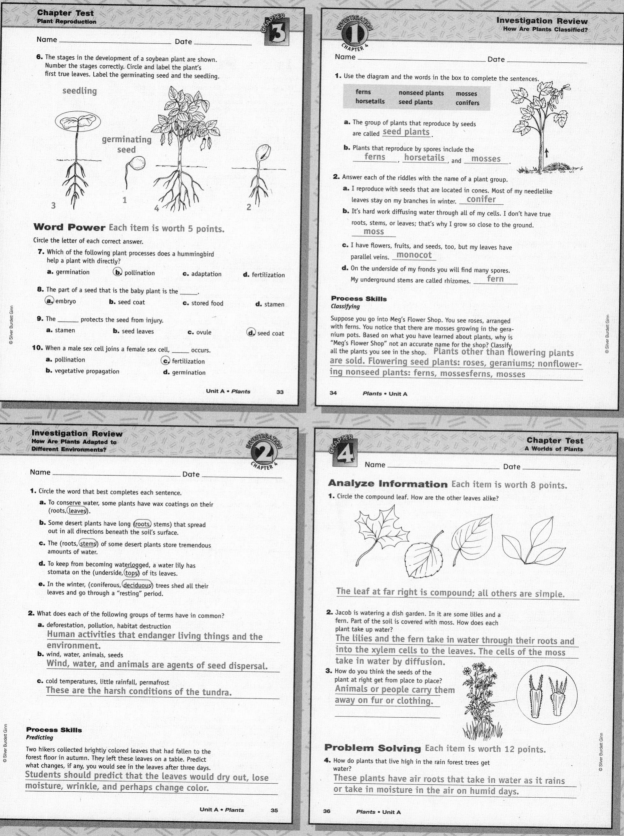

Chapter Test
Plant Reproduction

Name _____ Date _____

CHAPTER 3

6. The stages in the development of a soybean plant are shown. Number the stages correctly. Circle and label the plant's first true leaves. Label the germinating seed and the seedling.

seedling

germinating seed

3   1   4   2

Word Power Each item is worth 5 points.

Circle the letter of each correct answer.

7. Which of the following plant processes does a hummingbird help a plant with directly?
   a. germination   **b.** pollination   c. adaptation   d. fertilization

8. The part of a seed that is the baby plant is the _____.
   a. embryo   b. seed coat   c. stored food   d. stamen

9. The _____ protects the seed from injury.
   a. stamen   b. seed leaves   c. ovule   **d.** seed coat

10. When a male sex cell joins a female sex cell, _____ occurs.
    a. pollination   **c.** fertilization
    b. vegetative propagation   d. germination

Unit A • *Plants*   33

Investigation Review
How Are Plants Classified?

INVESTIGATION 1 CHAPTER 4

Name _____ Date _____

1. Use the diagram and the words in the box to complete the sentences.

| ferns | nonseed plants | mosses |
| horsetails | seed plants | conifers |

a. The group of plants that reproduce by seeds are called __seed plants__.

b. Plants that reproduce by spores include the __ferns__, __horsetails__, and __mosses__.

2. Answer each of the riddles with the name of a plant group.
   a. I reproduce with seeds that are located in cones. Most of my needlelike leaves stay on my branches in winter. __conifer__
   b. It's hard work diffusing water through all of my cells. I don't have true roots, stems, or leaves; that's why I grow so close to the ground. __moss__
   c. I have flowers, fruits, and seeds, too, but my leaves have parallel veins. __monocot__
   d. On the underside of my fronds you will find many spores. My underground stems are called rhizomes. __fern__

Process Skills
Classifying

Suppose you go into Meg's Flower Shop. You see roses, arranged with ferns. You notice that there are mosses growing in the geranium pots. Based on what you have learned about plants, why is "Meg's Flower Shop" not an accurate name for the shop? Classify all the plants you see in the shop. __Plants other than flowering plants are sold. Flowering seed plants: roses, geraniums; nonflowering nonseed plants: ferns, mossesferns, mosses__

34   *Plants* • Unit A

Investigation Review
How Are Plants Adapted to Different Environments?

INVESTIGATION 2 CHAPTER 4

Name _____ Date _____

1. Circle the word that best completes each sentence.
   a. To conserve water, some plants have wax coatings on their (roots, **leaves**).
   b. Some desert plants have long (**roots**, stems) that spread out in all directions beneath the soil's surface.
   c. The (roots, **stems**) of some desert plants store tremendous amounts of water.
   d. To keep from becoming waterlogged, a water lily has stomata on the (underside, **tops**) of its leaves.
   e. In the winter, (coniferous, **deciduous**) trees shed all their leaves and go through a "resting" period.

2. What does each of the following groups of terms have in common?
   a. deforestation, pollution, habitat destruction
      __Human activities that endanger living things and the environment.__
   b. wind, water, animals, seeds
      __Wind, water, and animals are agents of seed dispersal.__
   c. cold temperatures, little rainfall, permafrost
      __These are the harsh conditions of the tundra.__

Process Skills
Predicting

Two hikers collected brightly colored leaves that had fallen to the forest floor in autumn. They left these leaves on a table. Predict what changes, if any, you would see in the leaves after three days. __Students should predict that the leaves would dry out, lose moisture, wrinkle, and perhaps change color.__

Unit A • *Plants*   35

CHAPTER 4

Chapter Test
A Worlds of Plants

Name _____ Date _____

Analyze Information Each item is worth 8 points.

1. Circle the compound leaf. How are the other leaves alike?

   __The leaf at far right is compound; all others are simple.__

2. Jacob is watering a dish garden. In it are some lilies and a fern. Part of the soil is covered with moss. How does each plant take up water?
   __The lilies and the fern take in water through their roots and into the xylem cells to the leaves. The cells of the moss take in water by diffusion.__

3. How do you think the seeds of the plant at right get from place to place?
   __Animals or people carry them away on fur or clothing.__

Problem Solving Each item is worth 12 points.

4. How do plants that live high in the rain forest trees get water?
   __These plants have air roots that take in water as it rains or take in moisture in the air on humid days.__

36   *Plants* • Unit A

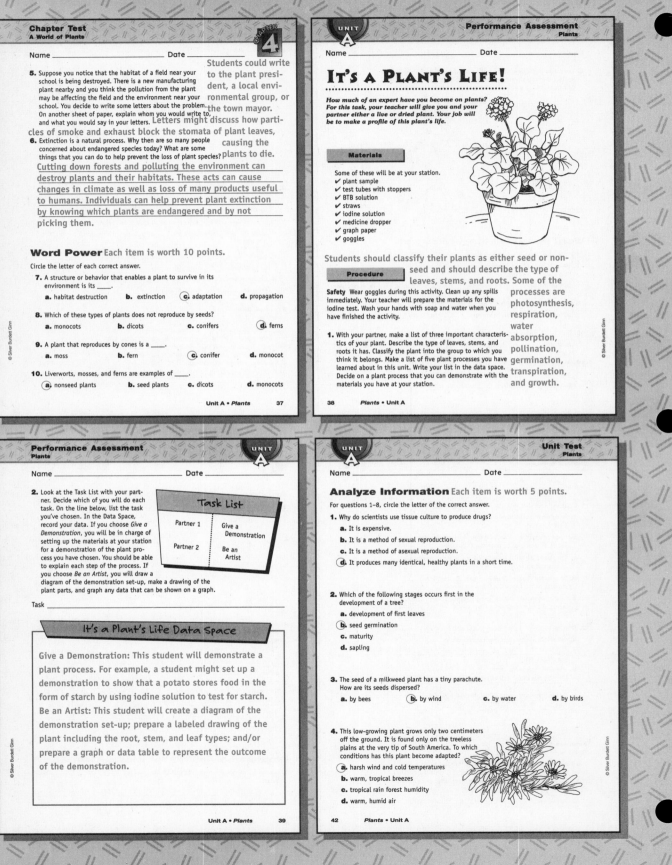

Chapter Test
A World of Plants

CHAPTER 4

Name _____ Date _____

5. Suppose you notice that the habitat of a field near your school is being destroyed. There is a new manufacturing plant nearby and you think the pollution from the plant may be affecting the field and the environment near your school. You decide to write some letters about the problem. On another sheet of paper, explain whom you would write to, and what you would say in your letters. **Students could write to the plant president, a local environmental group, or the town mayor. Letters might discuss how particles of smoke and exhaust block the stomata of plant leaves, causing the plants to die.**

6. Extinction is a natural process. Why then are so many people concerned about endangered species today? What are some things that you can do to help prevent the loss of plant species? **Cutting down forests and polluting the environment can destroy plants and their habitats. These acts can cause changes in climate as well as loss of many products useful to humans. Individuals can help prevent plant extinction by knowing which plants are endangered and by not picking them.**

Word Power Each item is worth 10 points.

Circle the letter of each correct answer.

7. A structure or behavior that enables a plant to survive in its environment is its _____.

   a. habitat destruction   b. extinction   c. adaptation   d. propagation

8. Which of these types of plants does not reproduce by seeds?

   a. monocots   b. dicots   c. conifers   d. ferns

9. A plant that reproduces by cones is a _____.

   a. moss   b. fern   c. conifer   d. monocot

10. Liverworts, mosses, and ferns are examples of _____.

    a. nonseed plants   b. seed plants   c. dicots   d. monocots

© Silver Burdett Ginn

UNIT A   **Performance Assessment**
Plants

Name _____ Date _____

IT'S A PLANT'S LIFE!

How much of an expert have you become on plants? For this task, your teacher will give you and your partner either a live or dried plant. Your job will be to make a profile of this plant's life.

Materials

Some of these will be at your station.
✔ plant sample
✔ test tubes with stoppers
✔ BTB solution
✔ straws
✔ iodine solution
✔ medicine dropper
✔ graph paper
✔ goggles

Procedure

Safety Wear goggles during this activity. Clean up any spills immediately. Your teacher will prepare the materials for the iodine test. Wash your hands with soap and water when you have finished the activity.

1. With your partner, make a list of three important characteristics of your plant. Describe the type of leaves, stems, and roots it has. Classify the plant into the group to which you think it belongs. Make a list of five plant processes you have learned about in this unit. Write your list in the data space. Decide on a plant process that you can demonstrate with the materials you have at your station.

Students should classify their plants as either seed or nonseed and should describe the type of leaves, stems, and roots. Some of the processes are photosynthesis, respiration, water absorption, pollination, germination, transpiration, and growth.

© Silver Burdett Ginn

Performance Assessment
Plants

UNIT A

Name _____ Date _____

2. Look at the Task List with your partner. Decide which of you will do each task. On the line below, list the task you've chosen. In the Data Space, record your data. If you choose *Give a Demonstration*, you will be in charge of setting up the materials at your station for a demonstration of the plant process you have chosen. You should be able to explain each step of the process. If you choose *Be an Artist*, you will draw a diagram of the demonstration set-up, make a drawing of the plant parts, and graph any data that can be shown on a graph.

Task _____

Task List

| Partner 1 | Give a Demonstration |
| Partner 2 | Be an Artist |

It's a Plant's Life Data Space

Give a Demonstration: This student will demonstrate a plant process. For example, a student might set up a demonstration to show that a potato stores food in the form of starch by using iodine solution to test for starch. Be an Artist: This student will create a diagram of the demonstration set-up; prepare a labeled drawing of the plant including the root, stem, and leaf types; and/or prepare a graph or data table to represent the outcome of the demonstration.

© Silver Burdett Ginn

UNIT A   **Unit Test**
Plants

Name _____ Date _____

Analyze Information Each item is worth 5 points.

For questions 1–8, circle the letter of the correct answer.

1. Why do scientists use tissue culture to produce drugs?

   a. It is expensive.
   b. It is a method of sexual reproduction.
   c. It is a method of asexual reproduction.
   d. It produces many identical, healthy plants in a short time.

2. Which of the following stages occurs first in the development of a tree?

   a. development of first leaves
   b. seed germination
   c. maturity
   d. sapling

3. The seed of a milkweed plant has a tiny parachute. How are its seeds dispersed?

   a. by bees   b. by wind   c. by water   d. by birds

4. This low-growing plant grows only two centimeters off the ground. It is found only on the treeless plains at the very tip of South America. To which conditions has this plant become adapted?

   a. harsh wind and cold temperatures
   b. warm, tropical breezes
   c. tropical rain forest humidity
   d. warm, humid air

© Silver Burdett Ginn

© Silver Burdett Ginn

Unit Test
Plants

© Silver Burdett Ginn

Name _____ Date _____

5. A commercial flower grower wants to have plants that look exactly alike. The best way for the grower to reproduce the plants is to _____.

a. have insects cross-pollinate the flowers

b. have birds pollinate them

(c.) do vegetative propagation

d. have wind carry the pollen to the flowers

6. In one season, an average field of corn takes in about 5 million liters of water and gives off about 4.5 million liters of water. How does all that water leave the plants?

a. It is released by stomata during photosynthesis.

(b.) It is released by stomata during transpiration.

c. It is combined with glucose.

d. It evaporates from the roots.

7. In some coral reefs in the Pacific Ocean, the crown of thorns starfish feeds on the tiny animals that live inside the coral. This eventually kills the coral and has had a harmful effect on the ocean environment. This starfish gets its energy during _____.

(a.) respiration

b. photosynthesis

c. transpiration

d. germination

8. In a food chain, the organisms on which all else depends are the _____.

a. decomposers

b. first-order consumers

(c.) producers

d. second-order consumers

Unit A • *Plants*   43

Unit Test
Plants

Name _____ Date _____

Problem Solving Each item is worth 6 points.

9. Describe three things you used today that came from plants.

Possible examples: cereals and bread made from grains, clothing made from plant fibers, furniture made of wood, and medicines derived from plants.

10. While hiking you see a hairy-cap moss that your guide book calls *Polytrichum commune*. As you travel up the mountain, you no longer see that species. Instead you see a related moss species called *Polytrichum juniperinum*. What is the probable reason for this change?

Answers should include that the habitat must be slightly different as you go up the mountain.

11. Native Americans of the Northeast used bark from birch trees to make canoes. What is bark, and why would it be a good material for this purpose?

Bark is the outermost covering of a tree's trunk. It is somewhat resistant to disease and fairly waterproof.

12. In some places in the United States, people are experimenting with naturalizing their lawn, or letting the native plants take over. What are the advantages or disadvantages in doing this?

Naturalizing encourages native species that may be endangered or on the decline because of ornamental planting. Native species require less water and fertilizer, both of which harm the environment. One disadvantage is that a naturalized lawn may not appear as beautiful as a neat cultivated lawn.

© Silver Burdett Ginn

44   *Plants* • Unit A

Unit Test
Earth's Land Resources

Name _____ Date _____

13. Look at the sketch of a cross section of a tree. Label the heartwood. Is the tree's approximate age nearer to your age, your parents' age, or the age your great-great grandparents would be today? How can you tell?

heartwood

The tree is about 35 years old, closest in age to the students' parents. Students can tell this by counting the annual rings.

14. Some beekeepers rent out their bees to people who own fruit orchards. Explain why.

Bees pollinate trees such as apple trees. Bees enter the flower, get pollen on their legs, and deposit it on the stigma of the pistil in the flower.

Word Power Each item is worth 4 points.

Match each term with its definition.

15. hydrotropism — a living thing that eats an herbivore

16. fruit — ground that is frozen all year long

17. xylem — structure that holds seeds

18. permafrost — asexual reproduction from part of a plant

19. vegetative propagation — water-conducting cells

20. second-order consumer — roots' growth toward water

© Silver Burdett Ginn

Unit A • *Plants*   45

Investigation Review
What Can You See in the Night Sky?

INVESTIGATION 1 CHAPTER 1

Name _____ Date _____

1. Use the words from the box to complete the paragraphs below.

Big Dipper	constellation	axis	Polaris
revolved		rotate	planets

Students gathered in the darkness of the planetarium. The first star pattern they recognized was the __Big Dipper__, which is part of a large __constellation__ called Ursa Major. As the stars moved across the night sky, they appeared to __rotate__ around one star, called __Polaris__. This is because this star is located directly above the northern tip of Earth's __axis__. Special effects in the planetarium allowed the students to see how different constellations looked during each season as Earth __revolved__ around the Sun. They also saw how __planets__, called "wandering stars" by the ancient Greeks, moved across the sky.

a. What causes different stars to appear in the sky at different times of the year?

Earth's revolution around the Sun

b. What makes the stars appear to move from east to west across the night sky?

Earth's rotation on its axis

Process Skills
Making Models, Interpreting Data

Explain how you could use a planisphere to demonstrate how the Big Dipper can sometimes appear upside down.

You could show that the Big Dipper sometimes looks upside down by turning the planisphere. The Big Dipper is in different positions at various times of the night and at various times of year because of Earth's rotation on its axis and its revolution around the Sun.

© Silver Burdett Ginn

46   *The Solar System and Beyond* • Unit B

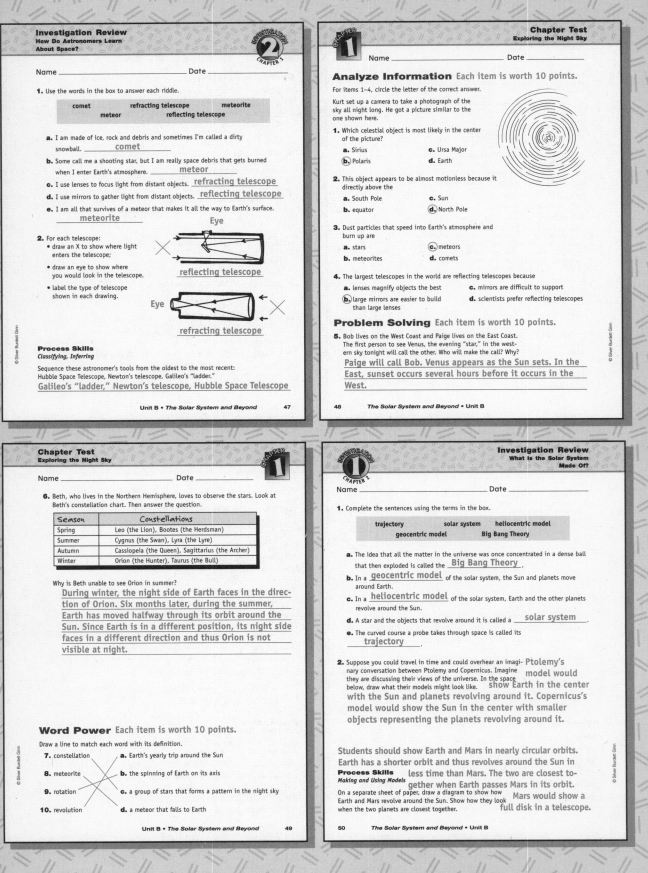

Answers

Investigation Review
How Do Astronomers Learn About Space?

Name _____ Date _____

CHAPTER 1 INVESTIGATION 2

1. Use the words in the box to answer each riddle.

comet	refracting telescope	meteorite
	meteor	reflecting telescope	

a. I am made of ice, rock and debris and sometimes I'm called a dirty snowball. _____comet_____

b. Some call me a shooting star, but I am really space debris that gets burned when I enter Earth's atmosphere. _____meteor_____

c. I use lenses to focus light from distant objects. _____refracting telescope_____

d. I use mirrors to gather light from distant objects. _____reflecting telescope_____

e. I am all that survives of a meteor that makes it all the way to Earth's surface. _____meteorite_____

2. For each telescope:
- draw an X to show where light enters the telescope;
- draw an eye to show where you would look in the telescope.
- label the type of telescope shown in each drawing.

Eye

_____reflecting telescope_____

Eye

_____refracting telescope_____

Process Skills
Classifying, Inferring

Sequence these astronomer's tools from the oldest to the most recent: Hubble Space Telescope, Newton's telescope, Galileo's "ladder."

Galileo's "ladder," Newton's telescope, Hubble Space Telescope

---

Chapter Test
Exploring the Night Sky

CHAPTER 1

Name _____ Date _____

Analyze Information Each item is worth 10 points.

For items 1–4, circle the letter of the correct answer.

Kurt set up a camera to take a photograph of the sky all night long. He got a picture similar to the one shown here.

1. Which celestial object is most likely in the center of the picture?

  a. Sirius   **c.** Ursa Major

  (b.) Polaris   **d.** Earth

2. This object appears to be almost motionless because it is directly above the

  a. South Pole   **c.** Sun

  b. equator   **(d.)** North Pole

3. Dust particles that speed into Earth's atmosphere and burn up are

  a. stars   **(c.)** meteors

  b. meteorites   **d.** comets

4. The largest telescopes in the world are reflecting telescopes because

  a. lenses magnify objects the best   **c.** mirrors are difficult to support

  (b.) large mirrors are easier to build than large lenses   **d.** scientists prefer reflecting telescopes

Problem Solving Each item is worth 10 points.

5. Bob lives on the West Coast and Paige lives on the East Coast. The first person to see Venus, the evening "star," in the western sky tonight will call the other. Who will make the call? Why?

Paige will call Bob. Venus appears as the Sun sets. In the East, sunset occurs several hours before it occurs in the West.

Chapter Test
Exploring the Night Sky

CHAPTER 1

Name _____ Date _____

6. Beth, who lives in the Northern Hemisphere, loves to observe the stars. Look at Beth's constellation chart. Then answer the question.

Season	Constellations
Spring	Leo (the Lion), Bootes (the Herdsman)
Summer	Cygnus (the Swan), Lyra (the Lyre)
Autumn	Cassiopeia (the Queen), Sagittarius (the Archer)
Winter	Orion (the Hunter), Taurus (the Bull)

Why is Beth unable to see Orion in summer?

During winter, the night side of Earth faces in the direction of Orion. Six months later, during the summer, Earth has moved halfway through its orbit around the Sun. Since Earth is in a different position, its night side faces in a different direction and thus Orion is not visible at night.

Word Power Each item is worth 10 points.

Draw a line to match each word with its definition.

7. constellation   **a.** Earth's yearly trip around the Sun

8. meteorite   **b.** the spinning of Earth on its axis

9. rotation   **c.** a group of stars that forms a pattern in the night sky

10. revolution   **d.** a meteor that falls to Earth

Investigation Review
What Is the Solar System Made Of?

INVESTIGATION 1 CHAPTER 2

Name _____ Date _____

1. Complete the sentences using the terms in the box.

trajectory	solar system	heliocentric model
	geocentric model	Big Bang Theory	

a. The idea that all the matter in the universe was once concentrated in a dense ball that then exploded is called the _Big Bang Theory_

b. In a _geocentric model_ of the solar system, the Sun and planets move around Earth.

c. In a _heliocentric model_ of the solar system, Earth and the other planets revolve around the Sun.

d. A star and the objects that revolve around it is called a _solar system_

e. The curved course a probe takes through space is called its _trajectory_.

2. Suppose you could travel in time and could overhear an imaginary conversation between Ptolemy and Copernicus. Imagine they are discussing their views of the universe. In the space below, draw what their models might look like.

Ptolemy's model would show Earth in the center with the Sun and planets revolving around it. Copernicus's model would show the Sun in the center with smaller objects representing the planets revolving around it.

Process Skills
Making and Using Models

On a separate sheet of paper, draw a diagram to show how Earth and Mars revolve around the Sun. Show how they look when the two planets are closest together.

Students should show Earth and Mars in nearly circular orbits. Earth has a shorter orbit and thus revolves around the Sun in less time than Mars. The two are closest together when Earth passes Mars in its orbit. Mars would show a full disk in a telescope.

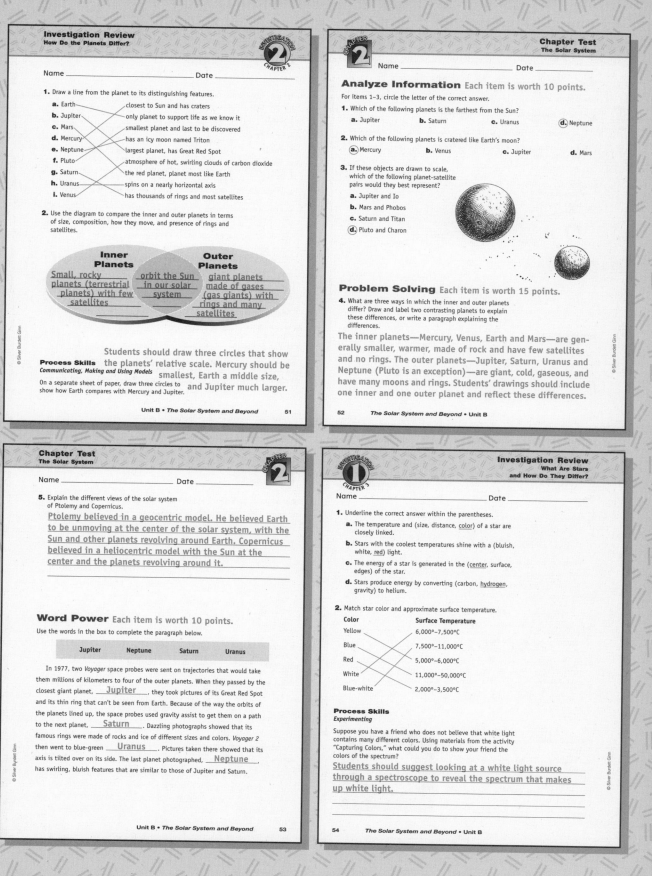

Investigation Review
How Do the Planets Differ?

INVESTIGATION 2 CHAPTER 2

Name _____ Date _____

1. Draw a line from the planet to its distinguishing features.

a. Earth — closest to Sun and has craters
b. Jupiter — only planet to support life as we know it
c. Mars — smallest planet and last to be discovered
d. Mercury — has an icy moon named Triton
e. Neptune — largest planet, has Great Red Spot
f. Pluto — atmosphere of hot, swirling clouds of carbon dioxide
g. Saturn — the red planet, planet most like Earth
h. Uranus — spins on a nearly horizontal axis
i. Venus — has thousands of rings and most satellites

2. Use the diagram to compare the inner and outer planets in terms of size, composition, how they move, and presence of rings and satellites.

Inner Planets
Small, rocky planets (terrestrial planets) with few satellites

orbit the Sun in our solar system

Outer Planets
giant planets made of gases (gas giants) with rings and many satellites

Process Skills
Communicating, Making and Using Models
On a separate sheet of paper, draw three circles to show how Earth compares with Mercury and Jupiter.

Students should draw three circles that show the planets' relative scale. Mercury should be smallest, Earth a middle size, and Jupiter much larger.

© Silver Burdett Ginn

Unit B • *The Solar System and Beyond* 51

CHAPTER 2

Chapter Test
The Solar System

Name _____ Date _____

Analyze Information Each item is worth 10 points.

For items 1–3, circle the letter of the correct answer.

1. Which of the following planets is the farthest from the Sun?

a. Jupiter   b. Saturn   c. Uranus   **d. Neptune**

2. Which of the following planets is cratered like Earth's moon?

a. Mercury   b. Venus   c. Jupiter   d. Mars

3. If these objects are drawn to scale, which of the following planet-satellite pairs would they best represent?

a. Jupiter and Io
b. Mars and Phobos
c. Saturn and Titan
d. Pluto and Charon

Problem Solving Each item is worth 15 points.

4. What are three ways in which the inner and outer planets differ? Draw and label two contrasting planets to explain these differences, or write a paragraph explaining the differences.

The inner planets—Mercury, Venus, Earth and Mars—are generally smaller, warmer, made of rock and have few satellites and no rings. The outer planets—Jupiter, Saturn, Uranus and Neptune (Pluto is an exception)—are giant, cold, gaseous, and have many moons and rings. Students' drawings should include one inner and one outer planet and reflect these differences.

© Silver Burdett Ginn

52 *The Solar System and Beyond* • Unit B

Chapter Test
The Solar System

CHAPTER 2

Name _____ Date _____

5. Explain the different views of the solar system of Ptolemy and Copernicus.

Ptolemy believed in a geocentric model. He believed Earth to be unmoving at the center of the solar system, with the Sun and other planets revolving around Earth. Copernicus believed in a heliocentric model with the Sun at the center and the planets revolving around it.

Word Power Each item is worth 10 points.

Use the words in the box to complete the paragraph below.

Jupiter	Neptune	Saturn	Uranus

In 1977, two *Voyager* space probes were sent on trajectories that would take them millions of kilometers to four of the outer planets. When they passed by the closest giant planet, **Jupiter**, they took pictures of its Great Red Spot and its thin ring that can't be seen from Earth. Because of the way the orbits of the planets lined up, the space probes used gravity assist to get them on a path to the next planet, **Saturn**. Dazzling photographs showed that its famous rings were made of rocks and ice of different sizes and colors. *Voyager 2* then went to blue-green **Uranus**. Pictures taken there showed that its axis is tilted over on its side. The last planet photographed, **Neptune**, has swirling, bluish features that are similar to those of Jupiter and Saturn.

© Silver Burdett Ginn

Unit B • *The Solar System and Beyond* 53

INVESTIGATION 1 CHAPTER 3

Investigation Review
What Are Stars and How Do They Differ?

Name _____ Date _____

1. Underline the correct answer within the parentheses.

a. The temperature and (size, distance, color) of a star are closely linked.

b. Stars with the coolest temperatures shine with a (bluish, white, red) light.

c. The energy of a star is generated in the (center, surface, edges) of the star.

d. Stars produce energy by converting (carbon, hydrogen, gravity) to helium.

2. Match star color and approximate surface temperature.

Color	Surface Temperature
Yellow	6,000°–7,500°C
Blue	7,500°–11,000°C
Red	5,000°–6,000°C
White	11,000°–50,000°C
Blue-white	2,000°–3,500°C

Process Skills
Experimenting

Suppose you have a friend who does not believe that white light contains many different colors. Using materials from the activity "Capturing Colors," what could you do to show your friend the colors of the spectrum?

Students should suggest looking at a white light source through a spectroscope to reveal the spectrum that makes up white light.

© Silver Burdett Ginn

54 *The Solar System and Beyond* • Unit B

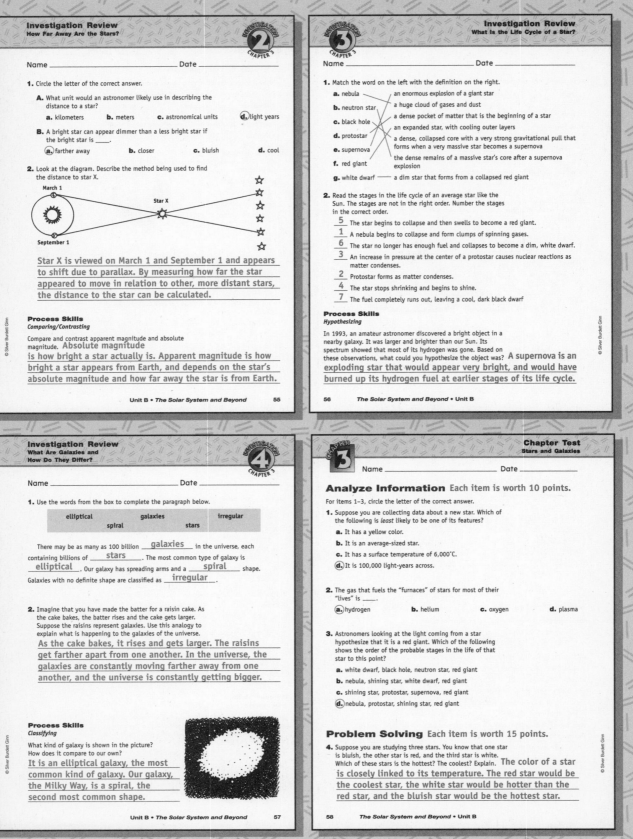

Answers

Investigation Review
How Far Away Are the Stars?

INVESTIGATION 2 · CHAPTER 3

Name _____ Date _____

1. Circle the letter of the correct answer.

A. What unit would an astronomer likely use in describing the distance to a star?

a. kilometers   b. meters   c. astronomical units   **d. light years**

B. A bright star can appear dimmer than a less bright star if the bright star is _____.

a. farther away   b. closer   c. bluish   d. cool

2. Look at the diagram. Describe the method being used to find the distance to star X.

March 1
September 1
Star X

Star X is viewed on March 1 and September 1 and appears to shift due to parallax. By measuring how far the star appeared to move in relation to other, more distant stars, the distance to the star can be calculated.

Process Skills
Comparing/Contrasting

Compare and contrast apparent magnitude and absolute magnitude. **Absolute magnitude is how bright a star actually is. Apparent magnitude is how bright a star appears from Earth, and depends on the star's absolute magnitude and how far away the star is from Earth.**

Unit B • The Solar System and Beyond   55

Investigation Review
What Is the Life Cycle of a Star?

INVESTIGATION 3 · CHAPTER 3

Name _____ Date _____

1. Match the word on the left with the definition on the right.

a. nebula — a huge cloud of gases and dust
b. neutron star — an enormous explosion of a giant star
c. black hole — a dense pocket of matter that is the beginning of a star
d. protostar — an expanded star, with cooling outer layers
e. supernova — a dense, collapsed core with a very strong gravitational pull that forms when a very massive star becomes a supernova
f. red giant — the dense remains of a massive star's core after a supernova explosion
g. white dwarf — a dim star that forms from a collapsed red giant

2. Read the stages in the life cycle of an average star like the Sun. The stages are not in the right order. Number the stages in the correct order.

5 The star begins to collapse and then swells to become a red giant.
1 A nebula begins to collapse and form clumps of spinning gases.
6 The star no longer has enough fuel and collapses to become a dim, white dwarf.
3 An increase in pressure at the center of a protostar causes nuclear reactions as matter condenses.
2 Protostar forms as matter condenses.
4 The star stops shrinking and begins to shine.
7 The fuel completely runs out, leaving a cool, dark black dwarf

Process Skills
Hypothesizing

In 1993, an amateur astronomer discovered a bright object in a nearby galaxy. It was larger and brighter than our Sun. Its spectrum showed that most of its hydrogen was gone. Based on these observations, what could you hypothesize the object was? **A supernova is an exploding star that would appear very bright, and would have burned up its hydrogen fuel at earlier stages of its life cycle.**

56   The Solar System and Beyond • Unit B

Investigation Review
What Are Galaxies and How Do They Differ?

INVESTIGATION 4 · CHAPTER 3

Name _____ Date _____

1. Use the words from the box to complete the paragraph below.

| elliptical | galaxies | irregular |
| spiral | stars | |

There may be as many as 100 billion **galaxies** in the universe, each containing billions of **stars**. The most common type of galaxy is **elliptical**. Our galaxy has spreading arms and a **spiral** shape. Galaxies with no definite shape are classified as **irregular**.

2. Imagine that you have made the batter for a raisin cake. As the cake bakes, the batter rises and the cake gets larger. Suppose the raisins represent galaxies. Use this analogy to explain what is happening to the galaxies of the universe. **As the cake bakes, it rises and gets larger. The raisins get farther apart from one another. In the universe, the galaxies are constantly moving farther away from one another, and the universe is constantly getting bigger.**

Process Skills
Classifying

What kind of galaxy is shown in the picture? How does it compare to our own? **It is an elliptical galaxy, the most common kind of galaxy. Our galaxy, the Milky Way, is a spiral, the second most common shape.**

Unit B • The Solar System and Beyond   57

Chapter Test
Stars and Galaxies

CHAPTER 3

Name _____ Date _____

Analyze Information Each item is worth 10 points.

For items 1–3, circle the letter of the correct answer.

1. Suppose you are collecting data about a new star. Which of the following is *least* likely to be one of its features?

a. It has a yellow color.
b. It is an average-sized star.
c. It has a surface temperature of 6,000°C.
d. It is 100,000 light-years across.

2. The gas that fuels the "furnaces" of stars for most of their "lives" is _____.

a. hydrogen   b. helium   c. oxygen   d. plasma

3. Astronomers looking at the light coming from a star hypothesize that it is a red giant. Which of the following shows the order of the probable stages in the life of that star to this point?

a. white dwarf, black hole, neutron star, red giant
b. nebula, shining star, white dwarf, red giant
c. shining star, protostar, supernova, red giant
d. nebula, protostar, shining star, red giant

Problem Solving Each item is worth 15 points.

4. Suppose you are studying three stars. You know that one star is bluish, the other star is red, and the third star is white. Which of these stars is the hottest? The coolest? Explain. **The color of a star is closely linked to its temperature. The red star would be the coolest star, the white star would be hotter than the red star, and the bluish star would be the hottest star.**

58   The Solar System and Beyond • Unit B

© Silver Burdett Ginn

190

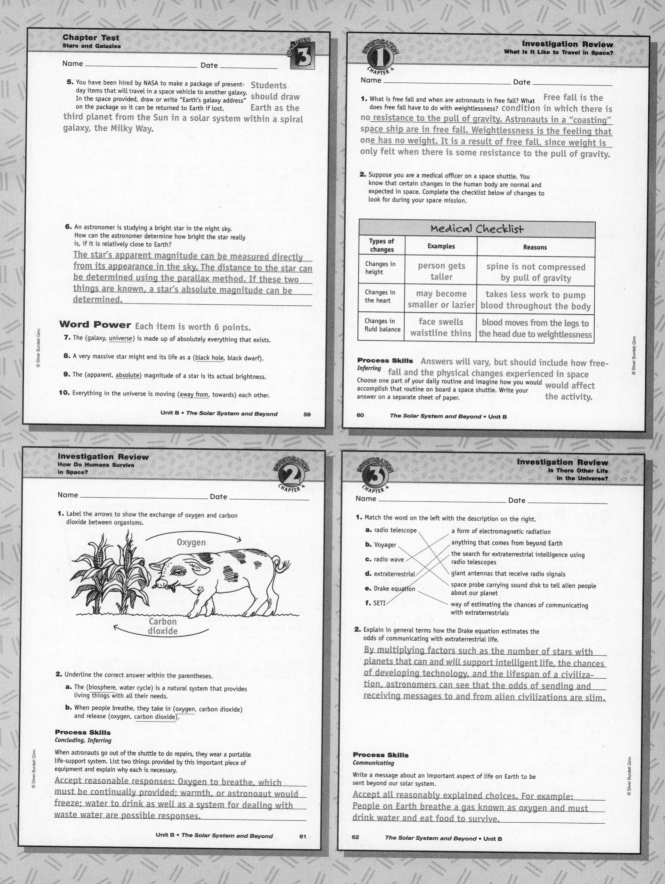

Answers

Chapter Test
Stars and Galaxies

CHAPTER 3

Name _____ Date _____

5. You have been hired by NASA to make a package of present-day items that will travel in a space vehicle to another galaxy. In the space provided, draw or write "Earth's galaxy address" on the package so it can be returned to Earth if lost.

Students should draw Earth as the third planet from the Sun in a solar system within a spiral galaxy, the Milky Way.

6. An astronomer is studying a bright star in the night sky. How can the astronomer determine how bright the star really is, if it is relatively close to Earth?

The star's apparent magnitude can be measured directly from its appearance in the sky. The distance to the star can be determined using the parallax method. If these two things are known, a star's absolute magnitude can be determined.

Word Power Each item is worth 6 points.

7. The (galaxy, <u>universe</u>) is made up of absolutely everything that exists.

8. A very massive star might end its life as a (<u>black hole</u>, black dwarf).

9. The (apparent, <u>absolute</u>) magnitude of a star is its actual brightness.

10. Everything in the universe is moving (<u>away from</u>, towards) each other.

Unit B • *The Solar System and Beyond*   59

Investigation Review
What Is It Like to Travel in Space?

INVESTIGATION 1 • CHAPTER 4

Name _____ Date _____

1. What is free fall and when are astronauts in free fall? What does free fall have to do with weightlessness?

Free fall is the condition in which there is no resistance to the pull of gravity. Astronauts in a "coasting" space ship are in free fall. Weightlessness is the feeling that one has no weight. It is a result of free fall, since weight is only felt when there is some resistance to the pull of gravity.

2. Suppose you are a medical officer on a space shuttle. You know that certain changes in the human body are normal and expected in space. Complete the checklist below of changes to look for during your space mission.

Medical Checklist

Types of changes	Examples	Reasons
Changes in height	person gets taller	spine is not compressed by pull of gravity
Changes in the heart	may become smaller or lazier	takes less work to pump blood throughout the body
Changes in fluid balance	face swells waistline thins	blood moves from the legs to the head due to weightlessness

Process Skills
Inferring
Choose one part of your daily routine and imagine how you would accomplish that routine on board a space shuttle. Write your answer on a separate sheet of paper.

Answers will vary, but should include how free-fall and the physical changes experienced in space would affect the activity.

60   *The Solar System and Beyond* • Unit B

Investigation Review
How Do Humans Survive in Space?

INVESTIGATION 2 • CHAPTER 4

Name _____ Date _____

1. Label the arrows to show the exchange of oxygen and carbon dioxide between organisms.

Oxygen

Carbon dioxide

2. Underline the correct answer within the parentheses.

a. The (<u>biosphere</u>, water cycle) is a natural system that provides living things with all their needs.

b. When people breathe, they take in (<u>oxygen</u>, carbon dioxide) and release (oxygen, <u>carbon dioxide</u>).

Process Skills
Concluding, Inferring

When astronauts go out of the shuttle to do repairs, they wear a portable life-support system. List two things provided by this important piece of equipment and explain why each is necessary.

Accept reasonable responses: Oxygen to breathe, which must be continually provided; warmth, or astronaut would freeze; water to drink as well as a system for dealing with waste water are possible responses.

Unit B • *The Solar System and Beyond*   61

Investigation Review
Is There Other Life in the Universe?

INVESTIGATION 3 • CHAPTER 4

Name _____ Date _____

1. Match the word on the left with the description on the right.

a. radio telescope — a form of electromagnetic radiation

b. Voyager — anything that comes from beyond Earth

c. radio wave — the search for extraterrestrial intelligence using radio telescopes

d. extraterrestrial — giant antennas that receive radio signals

e. Drake equation — space probe carrying sound disk to tell alien people about our planet

f. SETI — way of estimating the chances of communicating with extraterrestrials

2. Explain in general terms how the Drake equation estimates the odds of communicating with extraterrestrial life.

By multiplying factors such as the number of stars with planets that can and will support intelligent life, the chances of developing technology, and the lifespan of a civilization, astronomers can see that the odds of sending and receiving messages to and from alien civilizations are slim.

Process Skills
Communicating

Write a message about an important aspect of life on Earth to be sent beyond our solar system.

Accept all reasonably explained choices. For example: People on Earth breathe a gas known as oxygen and must drink water and eat food to survive.

62   *The Solar System and Beyond* • Unit B

Chapter Test
Living in Space

CHAPTER 4

Name _____ Date _____

Analyze Information Each item is worth 12 points.

For questions 1–2, circle the letter of the correct answer.

1. Astronauts who spend time on board a space shuttle experience several changes in their bodies. Which is the <u>least</u> likely to happen?

  a. a plugged-up nose   **c.** gain of muscle strength

  b. a slight gain in height   **d.** a slight loss of calcium

2. Which of the following is not one of the factors in the Drake equation?

  a. the ability to use sound to communicate   **c.** the number of habitable planets

  b. the average life span of a civilization   **d.** the number of planets that develop intelligent life

Problem Solving Each item is worth 12 points.

3. Suppose you are going to be in space for a very long time. Explain how you would provide and conserve oxygen on the trip.

Initial oxygen supplies would be brought in tanks. Bringing plants would allow carbon dioxide and oxygen to be cycled on board ship. Keeping EVA's and air lock use to a minimum would cut down on oxygen loss to space.

4. Each year students at Space Camp in Huntsville, Alabama, learn what it's like to be an astronaut in space. Suppose you were in charge of a space camp. List at least two programs that you would design to provide a realistic experience of life in space. Students' answers should include flight simulators and microgravity simulators, which would allow campers to experience what it feels like to be in space. They might also include some physical training to experience accomplishing daily functions in space.

© Silver Burdett Ginn

Chapter Test
Living in Space

CHAPTER 4

Name _____ Date _____

5. Make a list of things to take on a trip into space. Put a star by the most important choices.

Answers will vary but should reflect an understanding of the following basic needs of survival: oxygen, water, food, protection from extreme temperatures, and the need for an energy source to fuel both the spacecraft and life support systems.

6. Both you and your neighbor have lamps in your bedrooms. Suppose both lamps have timers that randomly turn the lights on for one second each day. How would you describe the conditions under which both lights would be on at the same time? Use this analogy to discuss the chances of communicating with intelligent extraterrestrial life.

Answers should include that the chances of both lamps being on simultaneously are slim. They should explain that the chances of communicating with intelligent life in the universe are also slim, given the conditions that must occur. Students may further summarize the Drake Equation.

Word Power Each item is worth 7 points.

Match each word on the left with its description on the right.

7. free fall — a feeling, experienced in free fall, that there is no gravity

8. extraterrestrial — self-contained and self-sustaining natural system

9. weightlessness — condition in which there is no resistance to the pull of gravity

10. biosphere — anything that comes from beyond Earth

© Silver Burdett Ginn

Performance Assessment
The Solar System and Beyond

UNIT B

Name _____ Date _____

OUR PLACE IN SPACE

Our space address is pretty easy to remember: Third planet from the Sun, Solar System, Milky Way Galaxy. Suppose you and your team want to demonstrate what this means to someone who has never studied the solar system. Your task will be to create a simple model to show where we are in space.

Materials

✔ crayons or markers
✔ several balls of different sizes
✔ text or reference books of constellation patterns

Procedure

1. You and your team will create a model of part of our solar system. As a team, choose two other planets besides Earth that you would like to include in your model. Also, choose one constellation that you wish to represent. On the lines below, list the planets and the constellation that you've chosen. Include the most distinguishing features about each. Students should list Earth and one other planet, and include information about their relative sizes, compositions, and distinguishing features. For the constellation, students should describe its shape and when visible from Earth.

© Silver Burdett Ginn

Performance Assessment
The Solar System and Beyond

UNIT B

Name _____ Date _____

2. Look at the Task List with your partners. Decide which of you will do each task. On the line below, list the task you've chosen. If you choose *Gather the Planets and Sun*, find several balls that best represent the planets you will model, based on their relative sizes. If you choose *Where in Relation to Sun*, determine where each planet in your model should be in relation to the Sun. If you choose *Show the Stars*, make a sketch of the constellation that your group has chosen. When you have completed your task, work together to draw a diagram in the Data Space to show how you would arrange these materials to make a useful model. Show how the planets, the Sun, and the constellation would have to be positioned in order to be visible from Earth.

Task List

• Gather the Planets and Sun

• Where in Relation to Sun

• Show the Stars

Task Student should list his or her task.

Our Place in Space Data Space

The Sun should be in the center of the Solar System. If Mercury or Venus is chosen, they must be placed to the right or left of the Sun, inside Earth's orbit. All other planets must be placed outside Earth's orbit. They must be placed such that they would be visible from the side of Earth facing away from the Sun—the night side. The constellation must be on the night side of Earth. Do not expect students to also compensate for seasonal changes.

© Silver Burdett Ginn

© Silver Burdett Ginn

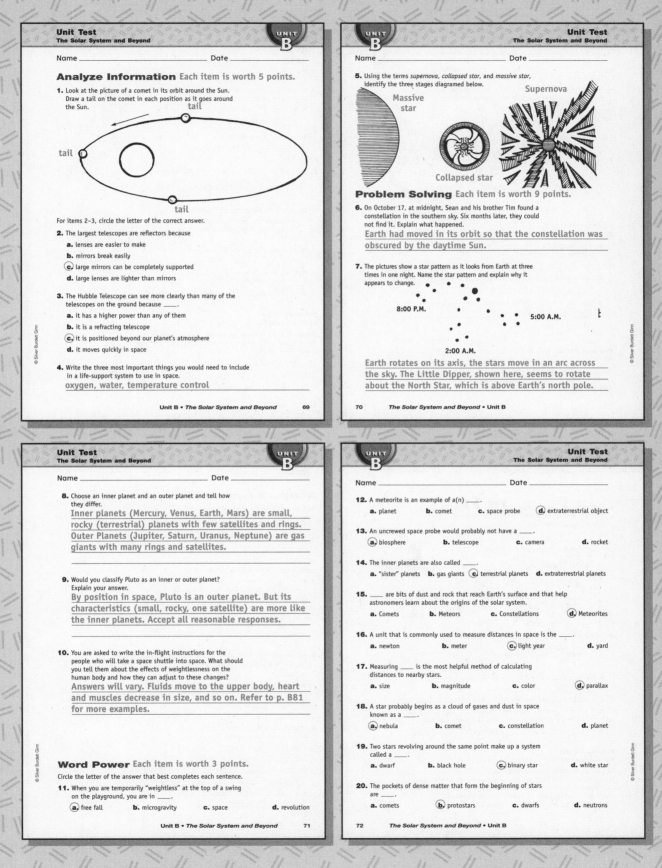

Answers

Unit Test
The Solar System and Beyond

Name _____ Date _____

Analyze Information Each item is worth 5 points.

1. Look at the picture of a comet in its orbit around the Sun. Draw a tail on the comet in each position as it goes around the Sun.

tail

tail

tail

For items 2–3, circle the letter of the correct answer.

2. The largest telescopes are reflectors because

a. lenses are easier to make

b. mirrors break easily

c. large mirrors can be completely supported

d. large lenses are lighter than mirrors

3. The Hubble Telescope can see more clearly than many of the telescopes on the ground because _____.

a. it has a higher power than any of them

b. it is a refracting telescope

c. it is positioned beyond our planet's atmosphere

d. it moves quickly in space

4. Write the three most important things you would need to include in a life-support system to use in space.

oxygen, water, temperature control

Unit B • The Solar System and Beyond 69

Unit Test
The Solar System and Beyond

5. Using the terms *supernova*, *collapsed star*, and *massive star*, identify the three stages diagrammed below.

Massive star

Supernova

Collapsed star

Problem Solving Each item is worth 9 points.

6. On October 17, at midnight, Sean and his brother Tim found a constellation in the southern sky. Six months later, they could not find it. Explain what happened.

Earth had moved in its orbit so that the constellation was obscured by the daytime Sun.

7. The pictures show a star pattern as it looks from Earth at three times in one night. Name the star pattern and explain why it appears to change.

8:00 P.M.

5:00 A.M.

2:00 A.M.

Earth rotates on its axis, the stars move in an arc across the sky. The Little Dipper, shown here, seems to rotate about the North Star, which is above Earth's north pole.

70 The Solar System and Beyond • Unit B

Unit Test
The Solar System and Beyond

Name _____ Date _____

8. Choose an inner planet and an outer planet and tell how they differ.

Inner planets (Mercury, Venus, Earth, Mars) are small, rocky (terrestrial) planets with few satellites and rings. Outer Planets (Jupiter, Saturn, Uranus, Neptune) are gas giants with many rings and satellites.

9. Would you classify Pluto as an inner or outer planet? Explain your answer.

By position in space, Pluto is an outer planet. But its characteristics (small, rocky, one satellite) are more like the inner planets. Accept all reasonable responses.

10. You are asked to write the in-flight instructions for the people who will take a space shuttle into space. What should you tell them about the effects of weightlessness on the human body and how they can adjust to these changes?

Answers will vary. Fluids move to the upper body, heart and muscles decrease in size, and so on. Refer to p. B81 for more examples.

Word Power Each item is worth 3 points.

Circle the letter of the answer that best completes each sentence.

11. When you are temporarily "weightless" at the top of a swing on the playground, you are in _____.

a. free fall   b. microgravity   c. space   d. revolution

Unit B • The Solar System and Beyond 71

Unit Test
The Solar System and Beyond

Name _____ Date _____

12. A meteorite is an example of a(n) _____.

a. planet   b. comet   c. space probe   d. extraterrestrial object

13. An uncrewed space probe would probably not have a _____.

a. biosphere   b. telescope   c. camera   d. rocket

14. The inner planets are also called _____.

a. "sister" planets   b. gas giants   c. terrestrial planets   d. extraterrestrial planets

15. _____ are bits of dust and rock that reach Earth's surface and that help astronomers learn about the origins of the solar system.

a. Comets   b. Meteors   c. Constellations   d. Meteorites

16. A unit that is commonly used to measure distances in space is the _____.

a. newton   b. meter   c. light year   d. yard

17. Measuring _____ is the most helpful method of calculating distances to nearby stars.

a. size   b. magnitude   c. color   d. parallax

18. A star probably begins as a cloud of gases and dust in space known as a _____.

a. nebula   b. comet   c. constellation   d. planet

19. Two stars revolving around the same point make up a system called a _____.

a. dwarf   b. black hole   c. binary star   d. white star

20. The pockets of dense matter that form the beginning of stars are _____.

a. comets   b. protostars   c. dwarfs   d. neutrons

72 The Solar System and Beyond • Unit B

Answers

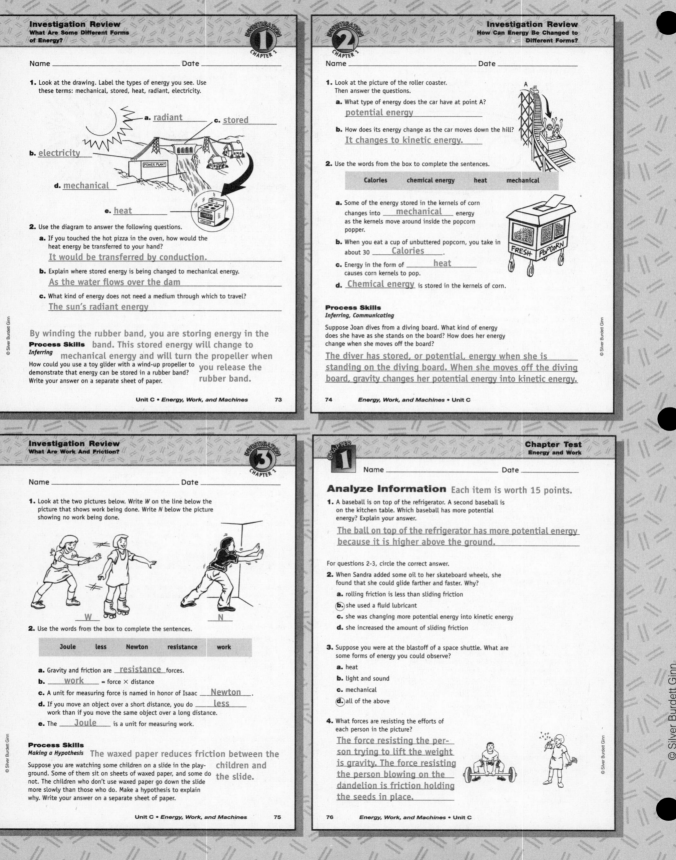

Investigation Review
What Are Some Different Forms of Energy?

1 CHAPTER 1

Name _____ Date _____

1. Look at the drawing. Label the types of energy you see. Use these terms: mechanical, stored, heat, radiant, electricity.

a. <u>radiant</u>   c. <u>stored</u>

b. <u>electricity</u>

d. <u>mechanical</u>

e. <u>heat</u>

POWER PLANT

2. Use the diagram to answer the following questions.

a. If you touched the hot pizza in the oven, how would the heat energy be transferred to your hand?

<u>It would be transferred by conduction.</u>

b. Explain where stored energy is being changed to mechanical energy.

<u>As the water flows over the dam</u>

c. What kind of energy does not need a medium through which to travel?

<u>The sun's radiant energy</u>

Process Skills
Inferring

How could you use a toy glider with a wind-up propeller to demonstrate that energy can be stored in a rubber band? Write your answer on a separate sheet of paper.

By winding the rubber band, you are storing energy in the band. This stored energy will change to mechanical energy and will turn the propeller when you release the rubber band.

Unit C • *Energy, Work, and Machines*   73

Investigation Review
How Can Energy Be Changed to Different Forms?

2 CHAPTER 1

Name _____ Date _____

1. Look at the picture of the roller coaster. Then answer the questions.

A

a. What type of energy does the car have at point A?
<u>potential energy</u>

b. How does its energy change as the car moves down the hill?
<u>It changes to kinetic energy.</u>

2. Use the words from the box to complete the sentences.

Calories	chemical energy	heat	mechanical

a. Some of the energy stored in the kernels of corn changes into <u>mechanical</u> energy as the kernels move around inside the popcorn popper.

b. When you eat a cup of unbuttered popcorn, you take in about 30 <u>Calories</u>.

FRESH POPCORN

c. Energy in the form of <u>heat</u> causes corn kernels to pop.

d. <u>Chemical energy</u> is stored in the kernels of corn.

Process Skills
Inferring, Communicating

Suppose Joan dives from a diving board. What kind of energy does she have as she stands on the board? How does her energy change when she moves off the board?

<u>The diver has stored, or potential, energy when she is standing on the diving board. When she moves off the diving board, gravity changes her potential energy into kinetic energy.</u>

74   *Energy, Work, and Machines* • Unit C

Investigation Review
What Are Work And Friction?

3 CHAPTER 1

Name _____ Date _____

1. Look at the two pictures below. Write *W* on the line below the picture that shows work being done. Write *N* below the picture showing no work being done.

W   N

2. Use the words from the box to complete the sentences.

Joule	less	Newton	resistance	work

a. Gravity and friction are <u>resistance</u> forces.

b. <u>work</u> = force × distance

c. A unit for measuring force is named in honor of Isaac <u>Newton</u>.

d. If you move an object over a short distance, you do <u>less</u> work than if you move the same object over a long distance.

e. The <u>Joule</u> is a unit for measuring work.

Process Skills
Making a Hypothesis

Suppose you are watching some children on a slide in the playground. Some of them sit on sheets of waxed paper, and some do not. The children who don't use waxed paper go down the slide more slowly than those who do. Make a hypothesis to explain why. Write your answer on a separate sheet of paper.

The waxed paper reduces friction between the children and the slide.

Unit C • *Energy, Work, and Machines*   75

Chapter Test
Energy and Work

CHAPTER 1

Name _____ Date _____

Analyze Information Each item is worth 15 points.

1. A baseball is on top of the refrigerator. A second baseball is on the kitchen table. Which baseball has more potential energy? Explain your answer.

<u>The ball on top of the refrigerator has more potential energy because it is higher above the ground.</u>

For questions 2-3, circle the correct answer.

2. When Sandra added some oil to her skateboard wheels, she found that she could glide farther and faster. Why?

a. rolling friction is less than sliding friction

(b.) she used a fluid lubricant

c. she was changing more potential energy into kinetic energy

d. she increased the amount of sliding friction

3. Suppose you were at the blastoff of a space shuttle. What are some forms of energy you could observe?

a. heat

b. light and sound

c. mechanical

(d.) all of the above

4. What forces are resisting the efforts of each person in the picture?

<u>The force resisting the person trying to lift the weight is gravity. The force resisting the person blowing on the dandelion is friction holding the seeds in place.</u>

76   *Energy, Work, and Machines* • Unit C

© Silver Burdett Ginn

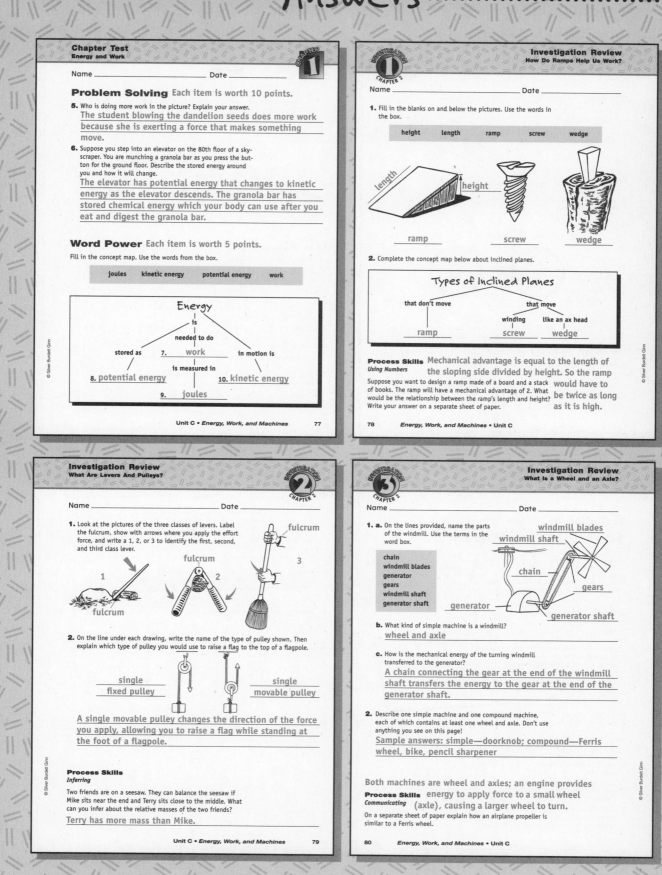

Chapter Test
Energy and Work

CHAPTER 1

Name _____ Date _____

Problem Solving Each item is worth 10 points.

5. Who is doing more work in the picture? Explain your answer.

The student blowing the dandelion seeds does more work
because she is exerting a force that makes something
move.

6. Suppose you step into an elevator on the 80th floor of a sky-
scraper. You are munching a granola bar as you press the button for the ground floor. Describe the stored energy around
you and how it will change.

The elevator has potential energy that changes to kinetic
energy as the elevator descends. The granola bar has
stored chemical energy which your body can use after you
eat and digest the granola bar.

Word Power Each item is worth 5 points.

Fill in the concept map. Use the words from the box.

| joules | kinetic energy | potential energy | work |

```
                    Energy
                      is
                 needed to do
    stored as      7.  work      in motion is
                is measured in
  8. potential energy          10. kinetic energy
               9.   joules
```

Unit C • Energy, Work, and Machines   77

INVESTIGATION 1
CHAPTER 2

Investigation Review
How Do Ramps Help Us Work?

Name _____ Date _____

1. Fill in the blanks on and below the pictures. Use the words in
the box.

| height | length | ramp | screw | wedge |

length / height

        ramp   screw   wedge

2. Complete the concept map below about inclined planes.

```
              Types of Inclined Planes
     that don't move              that move
                           winding    like an ax head
        ramp                screw          wedge
```

Process Skills
Using Numbers

Mechanical advantage is equal to the length of
the sloping side divided by height. So the ramp
would have to

Suppose you want to design a ramp made of a board and a stack
of books. The ramp will have a mechanical advantage of 2. What
would be the relationship between the ramp's length and height?
Write your answer on a separate sheet of paper.

be twice as long
as it is high.

78   Energy, Work, and Machines • Unit C

Investigation Review
What Are Levers And Pulleys?

INVESTIGATION 2
CHAPTER 2

Name _____ Date _____

1. Look at the pictures of the three classes of levers. Label
the fulcrum, show with arrows where you apply the effort
force, and write a 1, 2, or 3 to identify the first, second,
and third class lever.

fulcrum

fulcrum

1   fulcrum   2   3

fulcrum

2. On the line under each drawing, write the name of the type of pulley shown. Then
explain which type of pulley you would use to raise a flag to the top of a flagpole.

single   single
fixed pulley   movable pulley

A single movable pulley changes the direction of the force
you apply, allowing you to raise a flag while standing at
the foot of a flagpole.

Process Skills
Inferring

Two friends are on a seesaw. They can balance the seesaw if
Mike sits near the end and Terry sits close to the middle. What
can you infer about the relative masses of the two friends?

Terry has more mass than Mike.

Unit C • Energy, Work, and Machines   79

INVESTIGATION 3
CHAPTER 2

Investigation Review
What Is a Wheel and an Axle?

Name _____ Date _____

1. a. On the lines provided, name the parts
of the windmill. Use the terms in the
word box.

| chain
| windmill blades
| generator
| gears
| windmill shaft
| generator shaft

windmill blades
windmill shaft
chain
gears
generator
generator shaft

b. What kind of simple machine is a windmill?

wheel and axle

c. How is the mechanical energy of the turning windmill
transferred to the generator?

A chain connecting the gear at the end of the windmill
shaft transfers the energy to the gear at the end of the
generator shaft.

2. Describe one simple machine and one compound machine,
each of which contains at least one wheel and axle. Don't use
anything you see on this page!

Sample answers: simple—doorknob; compound—Ferris
wheel, bike, pencil sharpener

Both machines are wheel and axles; an engine provides

Process Skills
Communicating

energy to apply force to a small wheel
(axle), causing a larger wheel to turn.

On a separate sheet of paper explain how an airplane propeller is
similar to a Ferris wheel.

80   Energy, Work, and Machines • Unit C

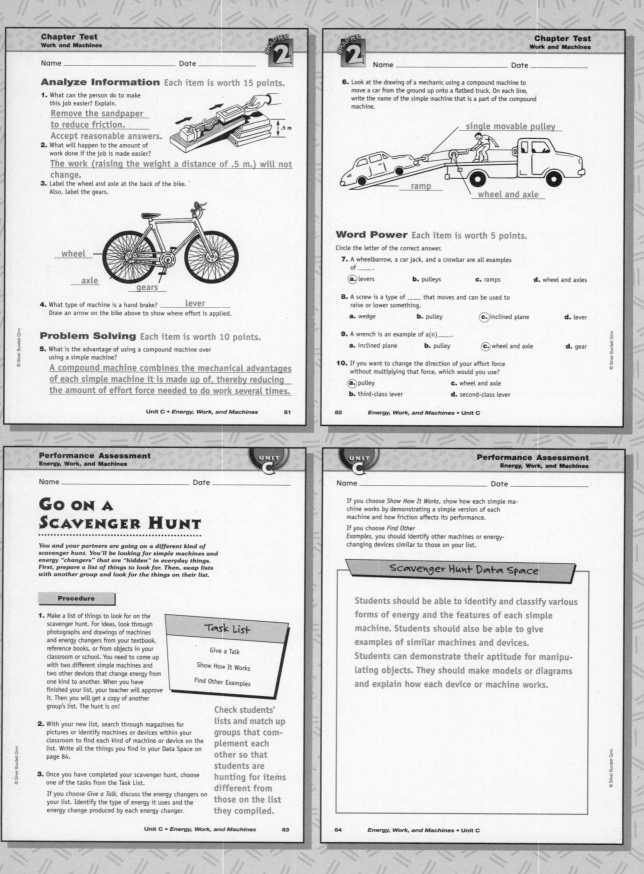

Chapter Test
Work and Machines

CHAPTER 2

Name _____ Date _____

Analyze Information Each item is worth 15 points.

1. What can the person do to make this job easier? Explain.

<u>Remove the sandpaper</u>
<u>to reduce friction.</u>
<u>Accept reasonable answers.</u>

2. What will happen to the amount of work done if the job is made easier?

<u>The work (raising the weight a distance of .5 m.) will not</u>
<u>change.</u>

3. Label the wheel and axle at the back of the bike. Also, label the gears.

wheel
axle
gears

4. What type of machine is a hand brake? _____ **lever** _____
Draw an arrow on the bike above to show where effort is applied.

Problem Solving Each item is worth 10 points.

5. What is the advantage of using a compound machine over using a simple machine?

<u>A compound machine combines the mechanical advantages</u>
<u>of each simple machine it is made up of, thereby reducing</u>
<u>the amount of effort force needed to do work several times.</u>

Unit C • *Energy, Work, and Machines*   81

Chapter Test
Work and Machines

CHAPTER 2

Name _____ Date _____

6. Look at the drawing of a mechanic using a compound machine to move a car from the ground up onto a flatbed truck. On each line, write the name of the simple machine that is a part of the compound machine.

single movable pulley

ramp

wheel and axle

Word Power Each item is worth 5 points.

Circle the letter of the correct answer.

7. A wheelbarrow, a car jack, and a crowbar are all examples of ____.

(a.) levers   **b.** pulleys   **c.** ramps   **d.** wheel and axles

8. A screw is a type of ____ that moves and can be used to raise or lower something.

a. wedge   **b.** pulley   **(c.)** inclined plane   **d.** lever

9. A wrench is an example of a(n)____.

a. inclined plane   **b.** pulley   **(c.)** wheel and axle   **d.** gear

10. If you want to change the direction of your effort force without multiplying that force, which would you use?

(a.) pulley   **c.** wheel and axle
b. third-class lever   **d.** second-class lever

82   *Energy, Work, and Machines* • Unit C

Performance Assessment
Energy, Work, and Machines

UNIT C

Name _____ Date _____

GO ON A SCAVENGER HUNT
··

You and your partners are going on a different kind of scavenger hunt. You'll be looking for simple machines and energy "changers" that are "hidden" in everyday things. First, prepare a list of things to look for. Then, swap lists with another group and look for the things on their list.

Procedure

1. Make a list of things to look for on the scavenger hunt. For ideas, look through photographs and drawings of machines and energy changers from your textbook, reference books, or from objects in your classroom or school. You need to come up with two different simple machines and two other devices that change energy from one kind to another. When you have finished your list, your teacher will approve it. Then you will get a copy of another group's list. The hunt is on!

Task List

Give a Talk

Show How It Works

Find Other Examples

Check students' lists and match up groups that complement each other so that students are hunting for items different from those on the list they compiled.

2. With your new list, search through magazines for pictures or identify machines or devices within your classroom to find each kind of machine or device on the list. Write all the things you find in your Data Space on page 84.

3. Once you have completed your scavenger hunt, choose one of the tasks from the Task List.

If you choose *Give a Talk*, discuss the energy changers on your list. Identify the type of energy it uses and the energy change produced by each energy changer.

Unit C • *Energy, Work, and Machines*   83

Performance Assessment
Energy, Work, and Machines

UNIT C

Name _____ Date _____

If you choose *Show How It Works*, show how each simple machine works by demonstrating a simple version of each machine and how friction affects its performance.

If you choose *Find Other Examples*, you should identify other machines or energy-changing devices similar to those on your list.

Scavenger Hunt Data Space

Students should be able to identify and classify various forms of energy and the features of each simple machine. Students should also be able to give examples of similar machines and devices.

Students can demonstrate their aptitude for manipulating objects. They should make models or diagrams and explain how each device or machine works.

84   *Energy, Work, and Machines* • Unit C

© Silver Burdett Ginn

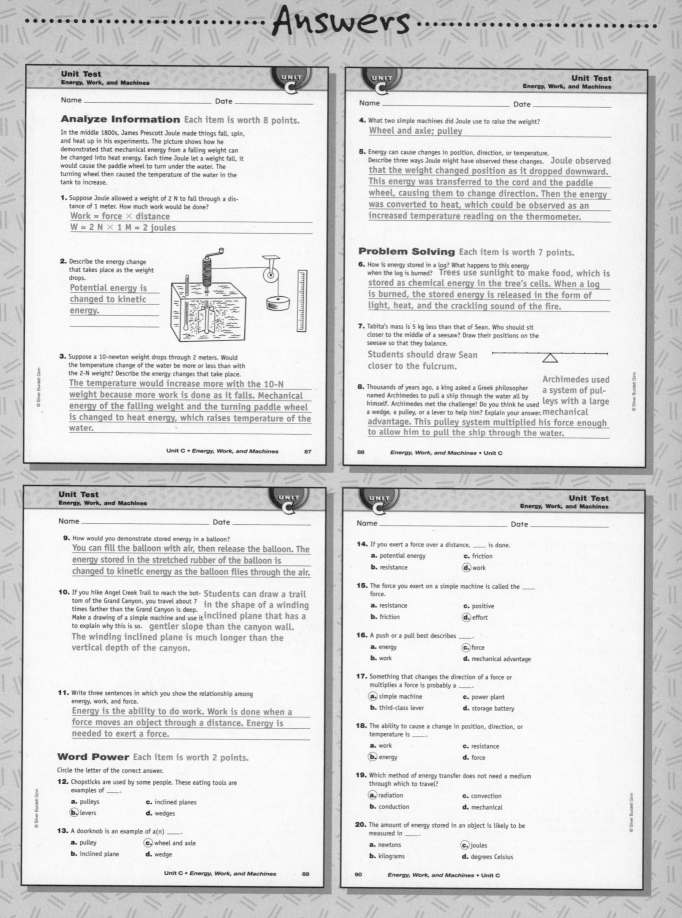

Unit Test
Energy, Work, and Machines

UNIT C

Name _____ Date _____

Analyze Information Each item is worth 8 points.

In the middle 1800s, James Prescott Joule made things fall, spin, and heat up in his experiments. The picture shows how he demonstrated that mechanical energy from a falling weight can be changed into heat energy. Each time Joule let a weight fall, it would cause the paddle wheel to turn under the water. The turning wheel then caused the temperature of the water in the tank to increase.

1. Suppose Joule allowed a weight of 2 N to fall through a distance of 1 meter. How much work would be done?
Work = force × distance
W = 2 N × 1 M = 2 joules

2. Describe the energy change that takes place as the weight drops.
Potential energy is changed to kinetic energy.

3. Suppose a 10-newton weight drops through 2 meters. Would the temperature change of the water be more or less than with the 2-N weight? Describe the energy changes that take place.
The temperature would increase more with the 10-N weight because more work is done as it falls. Mechanical energy of the falling weight and the turning paddle wheel is changed to heat energy, which raises temperature of the water.

Unit C • *Energy, Work, and Machines*   87

UNIT C

Unit Test
Energy, Work, and Machines

Name _____ Date _____

4. What two simple machines did Joule use to raise the weight?
Wheel and axle; pulley

5. Energy can cause changes in position, direction, or temperature. Describe three ways Joule might have observed these changes. Joule observed that the weight changed position as it dropped downward. This energy was transferred to the cord and the paddle wheel, causing them to change direction. Then the energy was converted to heat, which could be observed as an increased temperature reading on the thermometer.

Problem Solving Each item is worth 7 points.

6. How is energy stored in a log? What happens to this energy when the log is burned? Trees use sunlight to make food, which is stored as chemical energy in the tree's cells. When a log is burned, the stored energy is released in the form of light, heat, and the crackling sound of the fire.

7. Tabita's mass is 5 kg less than that of Sean. Who should sit closer to the middle of a seesaw? Draw their positions on the seesaw so that they balance.
Students should draw Sean closer to the fulcrum.

8. Thousands of years ago, a king asked a Greek philosopher named Archimedes to pull a ship through the water all by himself. Archimedes met the challenge! Do you think he used a wedge, a pulley, or a lever to help him? Explain your answer. Archimedes used a system of pulleys with a large mechanical advantage. This pulley system multiplied his force enough to allow him to pull the ship through the water.

88   *Energy, Work, and Machines* • Unit C

Unit Test
Energy, Work, and Machines

UNIT C

Name _____ Date _____

9. How would you demonstrate stored energy in a balloon?
You can fill the balloon with air, then release the balloon. The energy stored in the stretched rubber of the balloon is changed to kinetic energy as the balloon flies through the air.

10. If you hike Angel Creek Trail to reach the bottom of the Grand Canyon, you travel about 7 times farther than the Grand Canyon is deep. Make a drawing of a simple machine and use it to explain why this is so. Students can draw a trail in the shape of a winding inclined plane that has a gentler slope than the canyon wall. The winding inclined plane is much longer than the vertical depth of the canyon.

11. Write three sentences in which you show the relationship among energy, work, and force.
Energy is the ability to do work. Work is done when a force moves an object through a distance. Energy is needed to exert a force.

Word Power Each item is worth 2 points.

Circle the letter of the correct answer.

12. Chopsticks are used by some people. These eating tools are examples of _____.
a. pulleys
b. levers
c. inclined planes
d. wedges

13. A doorknob is an example of a(n) _____.
a. pulley
b. inclined plane
c. wheel and axle
d. wedge

Unit C • *Energy, Work, and Machines*   89

UNIT C

Unit Test
Energy, Work, and Machines

Name _____ Date _____

14. If you exert a force over a distance, _____ is done.
a. potential energy
b. resistance
c. friction
d. work

15. The force you exert on a simple machine is called the _____ force.
a. resistance
b. friction
c. positive
d. effort

16. A push or a pull best describes _____.
a. energy
b. work
c. force
d. mechanical advantage

17. Something that changes the direction of a force or multiplies a force is probably a _____.
a. simple machine
b. third-class lever
c. power plant
d. storage battery

18. The ability to cause a change in position, direction, or temperature is _____.
a. work
b. energy
c. resistance
d. force

19. Which method of energy transfer does not need a medium through which to travel?
a. radiation
b. conduction
c. convection
d. mechanical

20. The amount of energy stored in an object is likely to be measured in _____.
a. newtons
b. kilograms
c. joules
d. degrees Celsius

90   *Energy, Work, and Machines* • Unit C

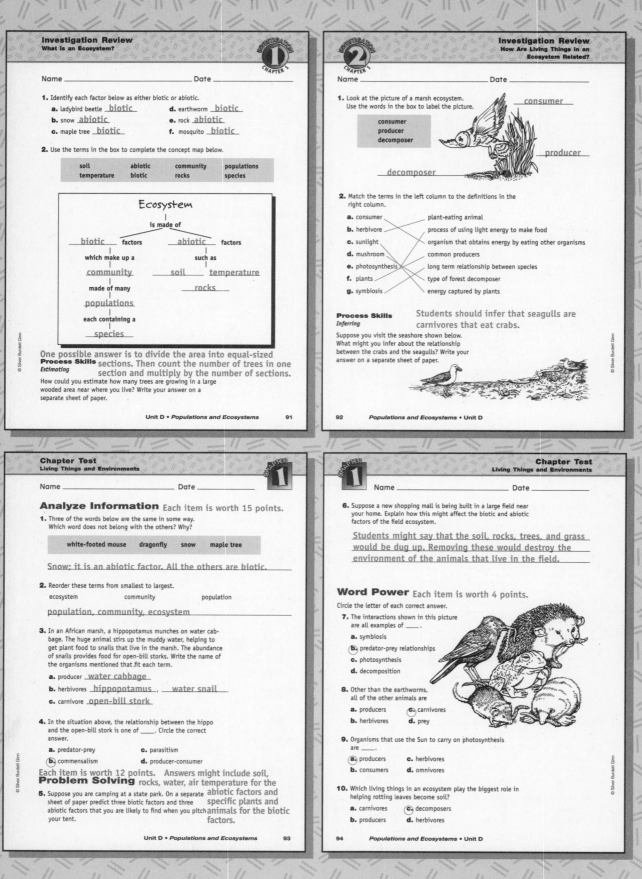

Investigation Review
What Is an Ecosystem?

INVESTIGATION 1 · CHAPTER 1

Name _____ Date _____

1. Identify each factor below as either biotic or abiotic.

   a. ladybird beetle _biotic_   d. earthworm _biotic_

   b. snow _abiotic_   e. rock _abiotic_

   c. maple tree _biotic_   f. mosquito _biotic_

2. Use the terms in the box to complete the concept map below.

| soil | abiotic | community | populations |
| temperature | biotic | rocks | species |

Ecosystem

is made of

biotic factors   _abiotic_ factors

which make up a   such as

community   _soil_   _temperature_

made of many   _rocks_

populations

each containing a

species

Process Skills
Estimating

One possible answer is to divide the area into equal-sized sections. Then count the number of trees in one section and multiply by the number of sections.

How could you estimate how many trees are growing in a large wooded area near where you live? Write your answer on a separate sheet of paper.

Unit D • Populations and Ecosystems   91

Investigation Review
How Are Living Things in an Ecosystem Related?

INVESTIGATION 2 · CHAPTER 1

Name _____ Date _____

1. Look at the picture of a marsh ecosystem. Use the words in the box to label the picture.

| consumer |
| producer |
| decomposer |

consumer

producer

decomposer

2. Match the terms in the left column to the definitions in the right column.

   a. consumer — plant-eating animal

   b. herbivore — process of using light energy to make food

   c. sunlight — organism that obtains energy by eating other organisms

   d. mushroom — common producers

   e. photosynthesis — long term relationship between species

   f. plants — type of forest decomposer

   g. symbiosis — energy captured by plants

Process Skills
Inferring

Students should infer that seagulls are carnivores that eat crabs.

Suppose you visit the seashore shown below. What might you infer about the relationship between the crabs and the seagulls? Write your answer on a separate sheet of paper.

92   Populations and Ecosystems • Unit D

Chapter Test
Living Things and Environments

CHAPTER 1

Name _____ Date _____

Analyze Information Each item is worth 15 points.

1. Three of the words below are the same in some way. Which word does not belong with the others? Why?

| white-footed mouse | dragonfly | snow | maple tree |

   Snow; it is an abiotic factor. All the others are biotic.

2. Reorder these terms from smallest to largest.

   ecosystem   community   population

   population, community, ecosystem

3. In an African marsh, a hippopotamus munches on water cabbage. The huge animal stirs up the muddy water, helping to get plant food to snails that live in the marsh. The abundance of snails provides food for open-bill storks. Write the name of the organisms mentioned that fit each term.

   a. producer _water cabbage_

   b. herbivores _hippopotamus_ , _water snail_

   c. carnivore _open-bill stork_

4. In the situation above, the relationship between the hippo and the open-bill stork is one of _____. Circle the correct answer.

   a. predator-prey   c. parasitism

   b. commensalism   d. producer-consumer

Problem Solving

Each item is worth 12 points.

5. Suppose you are camping at a state park. On a separate sheet of paper predict three biotic factors and three abiotic factors that you are likely to find when you pitch your tent.

Answers might include soil, rocks, water, air temperature for the abiotic factors and specific plants and animals for the biotic factors.

Unit D • Populations and Ecosystems   93

Chapter Test
Living Things and Environments

CHAPTER 1

Name _____ Date _____

6. Suppose a new shopping mall is being built in a large field near your home. Explain how this might affect the biotic and abiotic factors of the field ecosystem.

   Students might say that the soil, rocks, trees, and grass would be dug up. Removing these would destroy the environment of the animals that live in the field.

Word Power Each item is worth 4 points.

Circle the letter of each correct answer.

7. The interactions shown in this picture are all examples of _____.

   a. symbiosis

   b. predator-prey relationships

   c. photosynthesis

   d. decomposition

8. Other than the earthworms, all of the other animals are

   a. producers   c. carnivores

   b. herbivores   d. prey

9. Organisms that use the Sun to carry on photosynthesis are _____.

   a. producers   c. herbivores

   b. consumers   d. omnivores

10. Which living things in an ecosystem play the biggest role in helping rotting leaves become soil?

   a. carnivores   c. decomposers

   b. producers   d. herbivores

94   Populations and Ecosystems • Unit D

© Silver Burdett Ginn

198

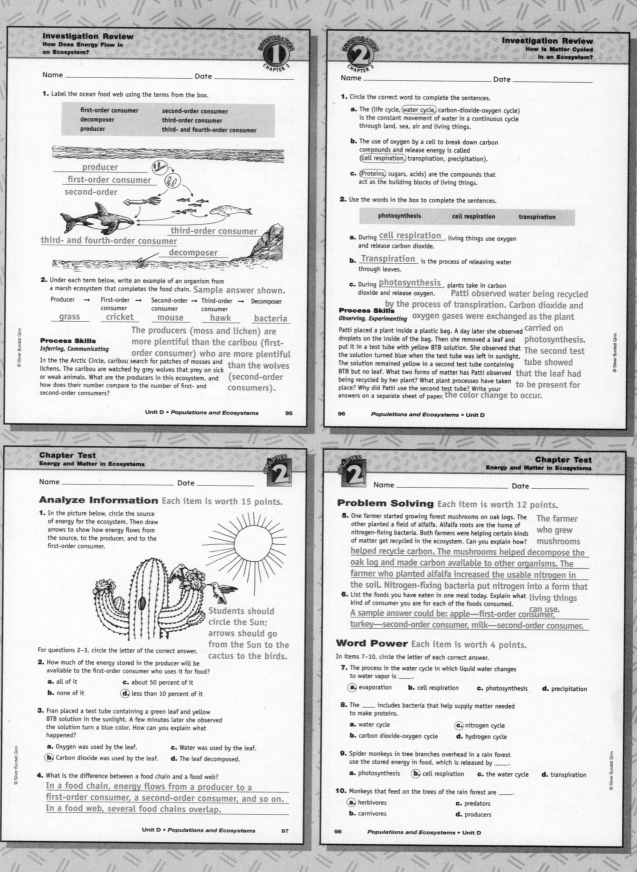

Investigation Review
How Does Energy Flow in
an Ecosystem?

INVESTIGATION 1 · CHAPTER 2

Name _____ Date _____

1. Label the ocean food web using the terms from the box.

first-order consumer   second-order consumer
decomposer   third-order consumer
producer   third- and fourth-order consumer

producer
first-order consumer
second-order
third-order consumer
third- and fourth-order consumer
decomposer

2. Under each term below, write an example of an organism from
a marsh ecosystem that completes the food chain. Sample answer shown.

Producer → First-order → Second-order → Third-order → Decomposer
            consumer   consumer   consumer

grass   cricket   mouse   hawk   bacteria

Process Skills
Inferring, Communicating

In the the Arctic Circle, caribou search for patches of mosses and
lichens. The caribou are watched by grey wolves that prey on sick
or weak animals. What are the producers in this ecosystem, and
how does their number compare to the number of first- and
second-order consumers?

The producers (moss and lichen) are
more plentiful than the caribou (first-
order consumer) who are more plentiful
than the wolves
(second-order
consumers).

© Silver Burdett Ginn

Unit D • Populations and Ecosystems   95

INVESTIGATION 2 · CHAPTER 2

Investigation Review
How Is Matter Cycled
in an Ecosystem?

Name _____ Date _____

1. Circle the correct word to complete the sentences.

a. The (life cycle, (water cycle,) carbon-dioxide-oxygen cycle)
is the constant movement of water in a continuous cycle
through land, sea, air and living things.

b. The use of oxygen by a cell to break down carbon
compounds and release energy is called
((cell respiration,) transpiration, precipitation).

c. ((Proteins,) sugars, acids) are the compounds that
act as the building blocks of living things.

2. Use the words in the box to complete the sentences.

photosynthesis   cell respiration   transpiration

a. During cell respiration , living things use oxygen
and release carbon dioxide.

b. Transpiration is the process of releasing water
through leaves.

c. During photosynthesis , plants take in carbon
dioxide and release oxygen.

Process Skills
Observing, Experimenting

Patti placed a plant inside a plastic bag. A day later she observed
droplets on the inside of the bag. Then she removed a leaf and
put it in a test tube with yellow BTB solution. She observed that
the solution turned blue when the test tube was left in sunlight.
The solution remained yellow in a second test tube containing
BTB but no leaf. What two forms of matter has Patti observed
being recycled by her plant? What plant processes have taken
place? Why did Patti use the second test tube? Write your
answers on a separate sheet of paper.

Patti observed water being recycled
by the process of transpiration. Carbon dioxide and
oxygen gases were exchanged as the plant
carried on
photosynthesis.
The second test
tube showed
that the leaf had
to be present for
the color change to occur.

© Silver Burdett Ginn

96   Populations and Ecosystems • Unit D

Chapter Test
Energy and Matter in Ecosystems

CHAPTER 2

Name _____ Date _____

Analyze Information Each item is worth 15 points.

1. In the picture below, circle the source
of energy for the ecosystem. Then draw
arrows to show how energy flows from
the source, to the producer, and to the
first-order consumer.

Students should
circle the Sun;
arrows should go
from the Sun to the
cactus to the birds.

For questions 2–3, circle the letter of the correct answer.

2. How much of the energy stored in the producer will be
available to the first-order consumer who uses it for food?

a. all of it   c. about 50 percent of it
b. none of it   (d.) less than 10 percent of it

3. Fran placed a test tube containing a green leaf and yellow
BTB solution in the sunlight. A few minutes later she observed
the solution turn a blue color. How can you explain what
happened?

a. Oxygen was used by the leaf.   c. Water was used by the leaf.
(b.) Carbon dioxide was used by the leaf.   d. The leaf decomposed.

4. What is the difference between a food chain and a food web?

In a food chain, energy flows from a producer to a
first-order consumer, a second-order consumer, and so on.
In a food web, several food chains overlap.

© Silver Burdett Ginn

Unit D • Populations and Ecosystems   97

CHAPTER 2

Chapter Test
Energy and Matter in Ecosystems

Name _____ Date _____

Problem Solving Each item is worth 12 points.

5. One farmer started growing forest mushrooms on oak logs. The
other planted a field of alfalfa. Alfalfa roots are the home of
nitrogen-fixing bacteria. Both farmers were helping certain kinds
of matter get recycled in the ecosystem. Can you explain how?

The farmer
who grew
mushrooms
helped recycle carbon. The mushrooms helped decompose the
oak log and made carbon available to other organisms. The
farmer who planted alfalfa increased the usable nitrogen in
the soil. Nitrogen-fixing bacteria put nitrogen into a form that

6. List the foods you have eaten in one meal today. Explain what
kind of consumer you are for each of the foods consumed.

living things
can use.

A sample answer could be: apple—first-order consumer,
turkey—second-order consumer, milk—second-order consumer.

Word Power Each item is worth 4 points.

In items 7–10, circle the letter of each correct answer.

7. The process in the water cycle in which liquid water changes
to water vapor is ____.

(a.) evaporation   b. cell respiration   c. photosynthesis   d. precipitation

8. The ____ includes bacteria that help supply matter needed
to make proteins.

a. water cycle   (c.) nitrogen cycle
b. carbon dioxide-oxygen cycle   d. hydrogen cycle

9. Spider monkeys in tree branches overhead in a rain forest
use the stored energy in food, which is released by ____.

a. photosynthesis   (b.) cell respiration   c. the water cycle   d. transpiration

10. Monkeys that feed on the trees of the rain forest are ____.

(a.) herbivores   c. predators
b. carnivores   d. producers

© Silver Burdett Ginn

98   Populations and Ecosystems • Unit D

Answers

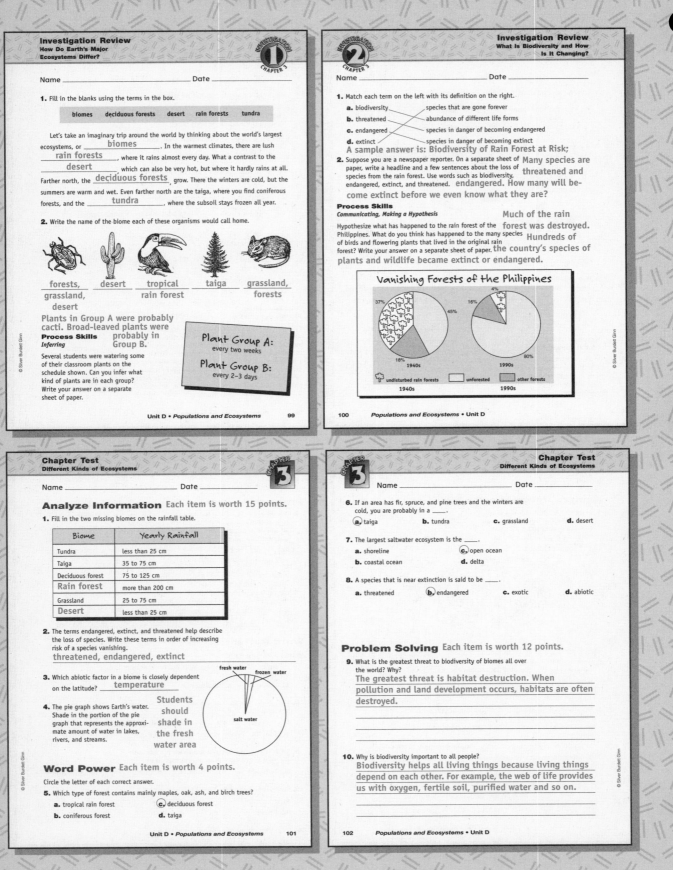

Investigation Review
How Do Earth's Major Ecosystems Differ?

INVESTIGATION 1 CHAPTER 3

Name _____ Date _____

1. Fill in the blanks using the terms in the box.

| biomes | deciduous forests | desert | rain forests | tundra |

Let's take an imaginary trip around the world by thinking about the world's largest ecosystems, or ___biomes___. In the warmest climates, there are lush ___rain forests___, where it rains almost every day. What a contrast to the ___desert___ which can also be very hot, but where it hardly rains at all. Farther north, the ___deciduous forests___ grow. There the winters are cold, but the summers are warm and wet. Even farther north are the taiga, where you find coniferous forests, and the ___tundra___, where the subsoil stays frozen all year.

2. Write the name of the biome each of these organisms would call home.

___forests, grassland, desert___   ___desert___   ___tropical rain forest___   ___taiga___   ___grassland, forests___

Plants in Group A were probably cacti. Broad-leaved plants were probably in Group B.

Process Skills
Inferring

Several students were watering some of their classroom plants on the schedule shown. Can you infer what kind of plants are in each group? Write your answer on a separate sheet of paper.

Plant Group A:
every two weeks

Plant Group B:
every 2–3 days

Investigation Review
What Is Biodiversity and How Is It Changing?

INVESTIGATION 2 CHAPTER 3

Name _____ Date _____

1. Match each term on the left with its definition on the right.

a. biodiversity — species that are gone forever
b. threatened — abundance of different life forms
c. endangered — species in danger of becoming endangered
d. extinct — species in danger of becoming extinct

A sample answer is: Biodiversity of Rain Forest at Risk;

2. Suppose you are a newspaper reporter. On a separate sheet of paper, write a headline and a few sentences about the loss of species from the rain forest. Use words such as biodiversity, endangered, extinct, and threatened. Many species are threatened and endangered. How many will become extinct before we even know what they are?

Process Skills
Communicating, Making a Hypothesis

Hypothesize what has happened to the rain forest of the Philippines. What do you think has happened to the many species of birds and flowering plants that lived in the original rain forest? Write your answer on a separate sheet of paper. Much of the rain forest was destroyed. Hundreds of the country's species of plants and wildlife became extinct or endangered.

Vanishing Forests of the Philippines

37%   45%   18%   1940s

4%   16%   80%   1990s

undisturbed rain forests   unforested   other forests

1940s   1990s

Chapter Test
Different Kinds of Ecosystems

CHAPTER 3

Name _____ Date _____

Analyze Information Each item is worth 15 points.

1. Fill in the two missing biomes on the rainfall table.

Biome	Yearly Rainfall
Tundra	less than 25 cm
Taiga	35 to 75 cm
Deciduous forest	75 to 125 cm
Rain forest	more than 200 cm
Grassland	25 to 75 cm
Desert	less than 25 cm

2. The terms endangered, extinct, and threatened help describe the loss of species. Write these terms in order of increasing risk of a species vanishing.
___threatened, endangered, extinct___

3. Which abiotic factor in a biome is closely dependent on the latitude? ___temperature___

4. The pie graph shows Earth's water. Shade in the portion of the pie graph that represents the approximate amount of water in lakes, rivers, and streams.

fresh water   frozen water   salt water

Students should shade in the fresh water area

Word Power Each item is worth 4 points.

Circle the letter of each correct answer.

5. Which type of forest contains mainly maples, oak, ash, and birch trees?
a. tropical rain forest   **c.** deciduous forest
b. coniferous forest   d. taiga

Chapter Test
Different Kinds of Ecosystems

CHAPTER 3

Name _____ Date _____

6. If an area has fir, spruce, and pine trees and the winters are cold, you are probably in a ___.
a. taiga   b. tundra   c. grassland   d. desert

7. The largest saltwater ecosystem is the ___.
a. shoreline   **c.** open ocean
b. coastal ocean   d. delta

8. A species that is near extinction is said to be ___.
a. threatened   **b.** endangered   c. exotic   d. abiotic

Problem Solving Each item is worth 12 points.

9. What is the greatest threat to biodiversity of biomes all over the world? Why?
The greatest threat is habitat destruction. When pollution and land development occurs, habitats are often destroyed.

10. Why is biodiversity important to all people?
Biodiversity helps all living things because living things depend on each other. For example, the web of life provides us with oxygen, fertile soil, purified water and so on.

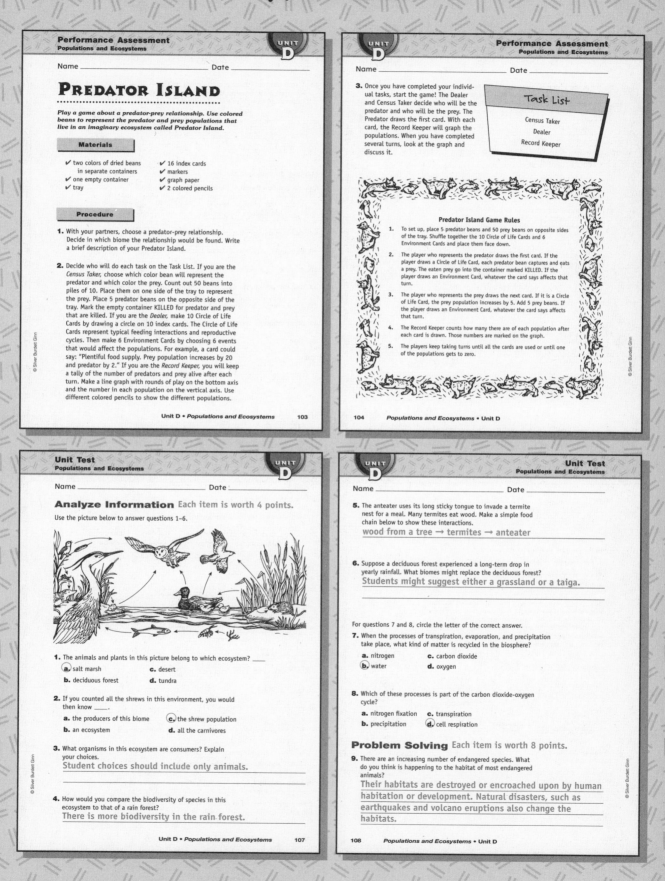

Performance Assessment
Populations and Ecosystems

UNIT D

Name _____ Date _____

PREDATOR ISLAND

Play a game about a predator-prey relationship. Use colored beans to represent the predator and prey populations that live in an imaginary ecosystem called Predator Island.

Materials

✔ two colors of dried beans in separate containers
✔ one empty container
✔ tray
✔ 16 index cards
✔ markers
✔ graph paper
✔ 2 colored pencils

Procedure

1. With your partners, choose a predator-prey relationship. Decide in which biome the relationship would be found. Write a brief description of your Predator Island.

2. Decide who will do each task on the Task List. If you are the *Census Taker*, choose which color bean will represent the predator and which color the prey. Count out 50 beans into piles of 10. Place them on one side of the tray to represent the prey. Place 5 predator beans on the opposite side of the tray. Mark the empty container KILLED for predator and prey that are killed. If you are the *Dealer*, make 10 Circle of Life Cards by drawing a circle on 10 index cards. The Circle of Life Cards represent typical feeding interactions and reproductive cycles. Then make 6 Environment Cards by choosing 6 events that would affect the populations. For example, a card could say: "Plentiful food supply. Prey population increases by 20 and predator by 2." If you are the *Record Keeper*, you will keep a tally of the number of predators and prey alive after each turn. Make a line graph with rounds of play on the bottom axis and the number in each population on the vertical axis. Use different colored pencils to show the different populations.

Unit D • Populations and Ecosystems   103

UNIT D

Performance Assessment
Populations and Ecosystems

Name _____ Date _____

3. Once you have completed your individual tasks, start the game! The Dealer and Census Taker decide who will be the predator and who will be the prey. The Predator draws the first card. With each card, the Record Keeper will graph the populations. When you have completed several turns, look at the graph and discuss it.

Task List

Census Taker
Dealer
Record Keeper

Predator Island Game Rules

1. To set up, place 5 predator beans and 50 prey beans on opposite sides of the tray. Shuffle together the 10 Circle of Life Cards and 6 Environment Cards and place them face down.

2. The player who represents the predator draws the first card. If the player draws a Circle of Life Card, each predator bean captures and eats a prey. The eaten prey go into the container marked KILLED. If the player draws an Environment Card, whatever the card says affects that turn.

3. The player who represents the prey draws the next card. If it is a Circle of Life Card, the prey population increases by 5. Add 5 prey beans. If the player draws an Environment Card, whatever the card says affects that turn.

4. The Record Keeper counts how many there are of each population after each card is drawn. Those numbers are marked on the graph.

5. The players keep taking turns until all the cards are used or until one of the populations gets to zero.

104   Populations and Ecosystems • Unit D

Unit Test
Populations and Ecosystems

UNIT D

Name _____ Date _____

Analyze Information Each item is worth 4 points.

Use the picture below to answer questions 1–6.

1. The animals and plants in this picture belong to which ecosystem? ____
   a. salt marsh   **c.** desert
   b. deciduous forest   **d.** tundra
   (a circled)

2. If you counted all the shrews in this environment, you would then know ____.
   a. the producers of this biome   **c.** the shrew population
   b. an ecosystem   **d.** all the carnivores
   (c circled)

3. What organisms in this ecosystem are consumers? Explain your choices.
   Student choices should include only animals.

4. How would you compare the biodiversity of species in this ecosystem to that of a rain forest?
   There is more biodiversity in the rain forest.

Unit D • Populations and Ecosystems   107

UNIT D

Unit Test
Populations and Ecosystems

Name _____ Date _____

5. The anteater uses its long sticky tongue to invade a termite nest for a meal. Many termites eat wood. Make a simple food chain below to show these interactions.
   wood from a tree → termites → anteater

6. Suppose a deciduous forest experienced a long-term drop in yearly rainfall. What biomes might replace the deciduous forest?
   Students might suggest either a grassland or a taiga.

For questions 7 and 8, circle the letter of the correct answer.

7. When the processes of transpiration, evaporation, and precipitation take place, what kind of matter is recycled in the biosphere?
   a. nitrogen   **c.** carbon dioxide
   b. water   **d.** oxygen
   (b circled)

8. Which of these processes is part of the carbon dioxide-oxygen cycle?
   a. nitrogen fixation   **c.** transpiration
   b. precipitation   **d.** cell respiration
   (d circled)

Problem Solving Each item is worth 8 points.

9. There are an increasing number of endangered species. What do you think is happening to the habitat of most endangered animals?
   Their habitats are destroyed or encroached upon by human habitation or development. Natural disasters, such as earthquakes and volcano eruptions also change the habitats.

108   Populations and Ecosystems • Unit D

© Silver Burdett Ginn

201

Answers

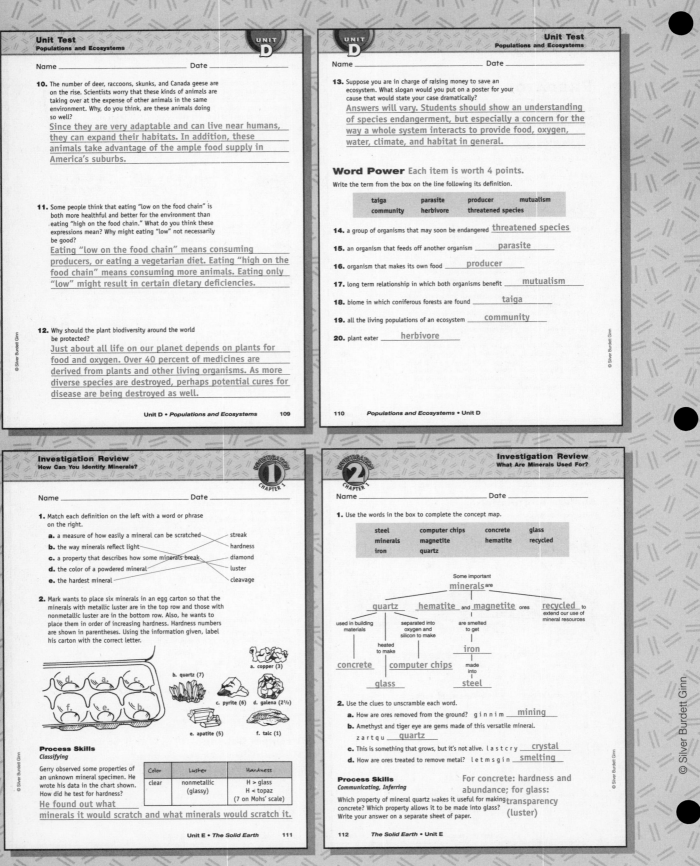

Unit Test
Populations and Ecosystems

UNIT D

Name _____ Date _____

10. The number of deer, raccoons, skunks, and Canada geese are on the rise. Scientists worry that these kinds of animals are taking over at the expense of other animals in the same environment. Why, do you think, are these animals doing so well?

Since they are very adaptable and can live near humans, they can expand their habitats. In addition, these animals take advantage of the ample food supply in America's suburbs.

11. Some people think that eating "low on the food chain" is both more healthful and better for the environment than eating "high on the food chain." What do you think these expressions mean? Why might eating "low" not necessarily be good?

Eating "low on the food chain" means consuming producers, or eating a vegetarian diet. Eating "high on the food chain" means consuming more animals. Eating only "low" might result in certain dietary deficiencies.

12. Why should the plant biodiversity around the world be protected?

Just about all life on our planet depends on plants for food and oxygen. Over 40 percent of medicines are derived from plants and other living organisms. As more diverse species are destroyed, perhaps potential cures for disease are being destroyed as well.

© Silver Burdett Ginn

Unit D • *Populations and Ecosystems*   109

UNIT D

Unit Test
Populations and Ecosystems

Name _____ Date _____

13. Suppose you are in charge of raising money to save an ecosystem. What slogan would you put on a poster for your cause that would state your case dramatically?

Answers will vary. Students should show an understanding of species endangerment, but especially a concern for the way a whole system interacts to provide food, oxygen, water, climate, and habitat in general.

Word Power Each item is worth 4 points.

Write the term from the box on the line following its definition.

taiga	parasite	producer	mutualism
community	herbivore	threatened species	

14. a group of organisms that may soon be endangered threatened species

15. an organism that feeds off another organism parasite

16. organism that makes its own food producer

17. long term relationship in which both organisms benefit mutualism

18. biome in which coniferous forests are found taiga

19. all the living populations of an ecosystem community

20. plant eater herbivore

© Silver Burdett Ginn

110   *Populations and Ecosystems* • Unit D

Investigation Review
How Can You Identify Minerals?

INVESTIGATION 1 · CHAPTER 1

Name _____ Date _____

1. Match each definition on the left with a word or phrase on the right.

   a. a measure of how easily a mineral can be scratched — streak
   b. the way minerals reflect light — hardness
   c. a property that describes how some minerals break — diamond
   d. the color of a powdered mineral — luster
   e. the hardest mineral — cleavage

2. Mark wants to place six minerals in an egg carton so that the minerals with metallic luster are in the top row and those with nonmetallic luster are in the bottom row. Also, he wants to place them in order of increasing hardness. Hardness numbers are shown in parentheses. Using the information given, label his carton with the correct letter.

   b. quartz (7)
   a. copper (3)
   c. pyrite (6)   d. galena (2½)
   e. apatite (5)   f. talc (1)

Process Skills
Classifying

Gerry observed some properties of an unknown mineral specimen. He wrote his data in the chart shown. How did he test for hardness?

Color	Luster	Hardness
clear	nonmetallic (glassy)	H > glass H < topaz (7 on Mohs' scale)

He found out what minerals it would scratch and what minerals would scratch it.

© Silver Burdett Ginn

Unit E • *The Solid Earth*   111

Investigation Review
What Are Minerals Used For?

INVESTIGATION 2 · CHAPTER 1

Name _____ Date _____

1. Use the words in the box to complete the concept map.

steel	computer chips	concrete	glass
minerals	magnetite	hematite	recycled
iron	quartz		

Some important
minerals are

quartz   **hematite** and **magnetite** ores   **recycled** to extend our use of mineral resources

used in building materials   separated into oxygen and silicon to make   are smelted to get

heated to make

iron

concrete   **computer chips**   made into

glass   **steel**

2. Use the clues to unscramble each word.

   a. How are ores removed from the ground? g i n n i m   mining
   b. Amethyst and tiger eye are gems made of this versatile mineral. z a r t q u   quartz
   c. This is something that grows, but it's not alive. l a s t c r y   crystal
   d. How are ores treated to remove metal? l e t m s g i n   smelting

Process Skills
Communicating, Inferring

Which property of mineral quartz makes it useful for making concrete? Which property allows it to be made into glass? Write your answer on a separate sheet of paper.

For concrete: hardness and abundance; for glass: transparency (luster)

© Silver Burdett Ginn

112   *The Solid Earth* • Unit E

© Silver Burdett Ginn

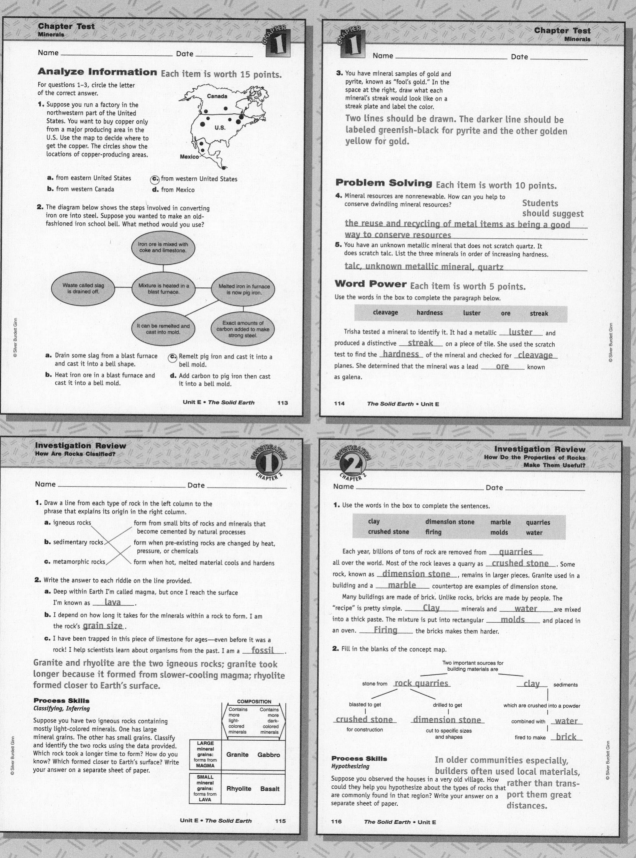

Chapter Test
Minerals

CHAPTER 1

Name _____ Date _____

Analyze Information Each item is worth 15 points.

For questions 1–3, circle the letter of the correct answer.

1. Suppose you run a factory in the northwestern part of the United States. You want to buy copper only from a major producing area in the U.S. Use the map to decide where to get the copper. The circles show the locations of copper-producing areas.

Canada
U.S.
Mexico

   a. from eastern United States   **c.** from western United States
   b. from western Canada   **d.** from Mexico

2. The diagram below shows the steps involved in converting iron ore into steel. Suppose you wanted to make an old-fashioned iron school bell. What method would you use?

- iron ore is mixed with coke and limestone.
- Waste called slag is drained off.
- Mixture is heated in a blast furnace.
- Melted iron in furnace is now pig iron.
- It can be remelted and cast into mold.
- Exact amounts of carbon added to make strong steel.

   a. Drain some slag from a blast furnace and cast it into a bell shape.
   b. Heat iron ore in a blast furnace and cast it into a bell mold.
   c. Remelt pig iron and cast it into a bell mold.
   d. Add carbon to pig iron then cast it into a bell mold.

© Silver Burdett Ginn

Unit E • The Solid Earth   **113**

CHAPTER 1

Chapter Test
Minerals

Name _____ Date _____

3. You have mineral samples of gold and pyrite, known as "fool's gold." In the space at the right, draw what each mineral's streak would look like on a streak plate and label the color.

Two lines should be drawn. The darker line should be labeled greenish-black for pyrite and the other golden yellow for gold.

Problem Solving Each item is worth 10 points.

4. Mineral resources are nonrenewable. How can you help to conserve dwindling mineral resources? **Students should suggest** the reuse and recycling of metal items as being a good way to conserve resources

5. You have an unknown metallic mineral that does not scratch quartz. It does scratch talc. List the three minerals in order of increasing hardness.
talc, unknown metallic mineral, quartz

Word Power Each item is worth 5 points.

Use the words in the box to complete the paragraph below.

cleavage	hardness	luster	ore	streak

Trisha tested a mineral to identify it. It had a metallic **luster** and produced a distinctive **streak** on a piece of tile. She used the scratch test to find the **hardness** of the mineral and checked for **cleavage** planes. She determined that the mineral was a lead **ore** known as galena.

© Silver Burdett Ginn

114   The Solid Earth • Unit E

Investigation Review
How Are Rocks Classified?

INVESTIGATION 1 CHAPTER 2

Name _____ Date _____

1. Draw a line from each type of rock in the left column to the phrase that explains its origin in the right column.

   a. igneous rocks — form from small bits of rocks and minerals that become cemented by natural processes
   b. sedimentary rocks — form when pre-existing rocks are changed by heat, pressure, or chemicals
   c. metamorphic rocks — form when hot, melted material cools and hardens

2. Write the answer to each riddle on the line provided.
   a. Deep within Earth I'm called magma, but once I reach the surface I'm known as ___lava___.
   b. I depend on how long it takes for the minerals within a rock to form. I am the rock's _grain size_.
   c. I have been trapped in this piece of limestone for ages—even before it was a rock! I help scientists learn about organisms from the past. I am a ___fossil___.

Granite and rhyolite are the two igneous rocks; granite took longer because it formed from slower-cooling magma; rhyolite formed closer to Earth's surface.

Process Skills
Classifying, Inferring

Suppose you have two igneous rocks containing mostly light-colored minerals. One has large mineral grains. The other has small grains. Classify and identify the two rocks using the data provided. Which rock took a longer time to form? How do you know? Which formed closer to Earth's surface? Write your answer on a separate sheet of paper.

	COMPOSITION	
	Contains more light-colored minerals	Contains more dark-colored minerals
LARGE mineral grains: forms from MAGMA	Granite	Gabbro
SMALL mineral grains: forms from LAVA	Rhyolite	Basalt

© Silver Burdett Ginn

Unit E • The Solid Earth   **115**

INVESTIGATION 2 CHAPTER 2

Investigation Review
How Do the Properties of Rocks Make Them Useful?

Name _____ Date _____

1. Use the words in the box to complete the sentences.

clay	dimension stone	marble	quarries
crushed stone	firing	molds	water

Each year, billions of tons of rock are removed from **quarries** all over the world. Most of the rock leaves a quarry as **crushed stone**. Some rock, known as **dimension stone**, remains in larger pieces. Granite used in a building and a **marble** countertop are examples of dimension stone.

Many buildings are made of brick. Unlike rocks, bricks are made by people. The "recipe" is pretty simple. **Clay** minerals and **water** are mixed into a thick paste. The mixture is put into rectangular **molds** and placed in an oven. **Firing** the bricks makes them harder.

2. Fill in the blanks of the concept map.

Two important sources for building materials are

stone from **rock quarries**   **clay** sediments

blasted to get   drilled to get   which are crushed into a powder

crushed stone for construction   **dimension stone** cut to specific sizes and shapes   combined with **water**

fired to make **brick**

Process Skills
Hypothesizing

In older communities especially, builders often used local materials, rather than trans-port them great distances.

Suppose you observed the houses in a very old village. How could they help you hypothesize about the types of rocks that are commonly found in that region? Write your answer on a separate sheet of paper.

© Silver Burdett Ginn

116   The Solid Earth • Unit E

© Silver Burdett Ginn

Answers

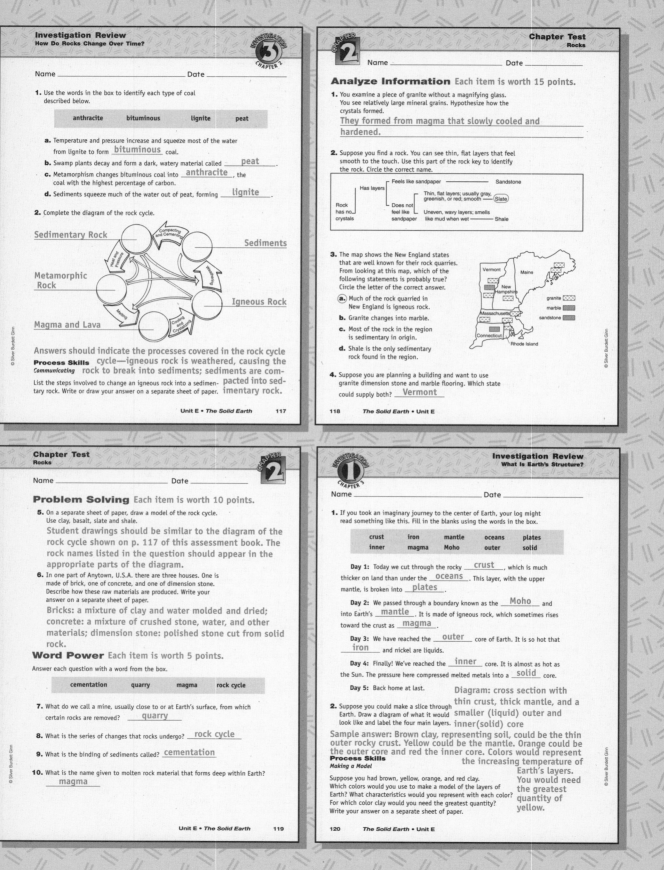

Investigation Review
How Do Rocks Change Over Time?

INVESTIGATION 3 CHAPTER 2

Name _____ Date _____

1. Use the words in the box to identify each type of coal described below.

| anthracite | bituminous | lignite | peat |

   a. Temperature and pressure increase and squeeze most of the water from lignite to form **bituminous** coal.
   b. Swamp plants decay and form a dark, watery material called **peat**.
   c. Metamorphism changes bituminous coal into **anthracite**, the coal with the highest percentage of carbon.
   d. Sediments squeeze much of the water out of peat, forming **lignite**.

2. Complete the diagram of the rock cycle.

Sedimentary Rock

Compacting and Cementing

Sediments

Heat and Pressure

Weathering

Metamorphic Rock

Igneous Rock

Melting

Cooling and Crystallizing

Magma and Lava

Process Skills
Communicating

List the steps involved to change an igneous rock into a sedimentary rock. Write or draw your answer on a separate sheet of paper.

Answers should indicate the processes covered in the rock cycle—igneous rock is weathered, causing the rock to break into sediments; sediments are compacted into sedimentary rock.

CHAPTER 2

Chapter Test
Rocks

Name _____ Date _____

Analyze Information Each item is worth 15 points.

1. You examine a piece of granite without a magnifying glass. You see relatively large mineral grains. Hypothesize how the crystals formed.
   They formed from magma that slowly cooled and hardened.

2. Suppose you find a rock. You can see thin, flat layers that feel smooth to the touch. Use this part of the rock key to identify the rock. Circle the correct name.

   Rock has no crystals
   - Has layers
     - Feels like sandpaper —— Sandstone
     - Does not feel like sandpaper
       - Thin, flat layers; usually gray, greenish, or red; smooth —— (Slate)
       - Uneven, wavy layers; smells like mud when wet —— Shale

3. The map shows the New England states that are well known for their rock quarries. From looking at this map, which of the following statements is probably true? Circle the letter of the correct answer.

   a. Much of the rock quarried in New England is igneous rock.
   b. Granite changes into marble.
   c. Most of the rock in the region is sedimentary in origin.
   d. Shale is the only sedimentary rock found in the region.

   Vermont, Maine, New Hampshire, Massachusetts, Connecticut, Rhode Island
   granite, marble, sandstone

4. Suppose you are planning a building and want to use granite dimension stone and marble flooring. Which state could supply both? **Vermont**

Chapter Test
Rocks

CHAPTER 2

Name _____ Date _____

Problem Solving Each item is worth 10 points.

5. On a separate sheet of paper, draw a model of the rock cycle. Use clay, basalt, slate and shale.
   Student drawings should be similar to the diagram of the rock cycle shown on p. 117 of this assessment book. The rock names listed in the question should appear in the appropriate parts of the diagram.

6. In one part of Anytown, U.S.A. there are three houses. One is made of brick, one of concrete, and one of dimension stone. Describe how these raw materials are produced. Write your answer on a separate sheet of paper.
   Bricks: a mixture of clay and water molded and dried; concrete: a mixture of crushed stone, water, and other materials; dimension stone: polished stone cut from solid rock.

Word Power Each item is worth 5 points.

Answer each question with a word from the box.

| cementation | quarry | magma | rock cycle |

7. What do we call a mine, usually close to or at Earth's surface, from which certain rocks are removed? **quarry**

8. What is the series of changes that rocks undergo? **rock cycle**

9. What is the binding of sediments called? **cementation**

10. What is the name given to molten rock material that forms deep within Earth? **magma**

INVESTIGATION 1 CHAPTER 3

Investigation Review
What Is Earth's Structure?

Name _____ Date _____

1. If you took an imaginary journey to the center of Earth, your log might read something like this. Fill in the blanks using the words in the box.

| crust | iron | mantle | oceans | plates |
| inner | magma | Moho | outer | solid |

   Day 1: Today we cut through the rocky **crust**, which is much thicker on land than under the **oceans**. This layer, with the upper mantle, is broken into **plates**.

   Day 2: We passed through a boundary known as the **Moho** and into Earth's **mantle**. It is made of igneous rock, which sometimes rises toward the crust as **magma**.

   Day 3: We have reached the **outer** core of Earth. It is so hot that **iron** and nickel are liquids.

   Day 4: Finally! We've reached the **inner** core. It is almost as hot as the Sun. The pressure here compressed melted metals into a **solid** core.

   Day 5: Back home at last.

2. Suppose you could make a slice through Earth. Draw a diagram of what it would look like and label the four main layers.

   Diagram: cross section with thin crust, thick mantle, and a smaller (liquid) outer and inner(solid) core

   Sample answer: Brown clay, representing soil, could be the thin outer rocky crust. Yellow could be the mantle. Orange could be the outer core and red the inner core. Colors would represent the increasing temperature of Earth's layers. You would need the greatest quantity of yellow.

Process Skills
Making a Model

Suppose you had brown, yellow, orange, and red clay. Which colors would you use to make a model of the layers of Earth? What characteristics would you represent with each color? For which color clay would you need the greatest quantity? Write your answer on a separate sheet of paper.

© Silver Burdett Ginn

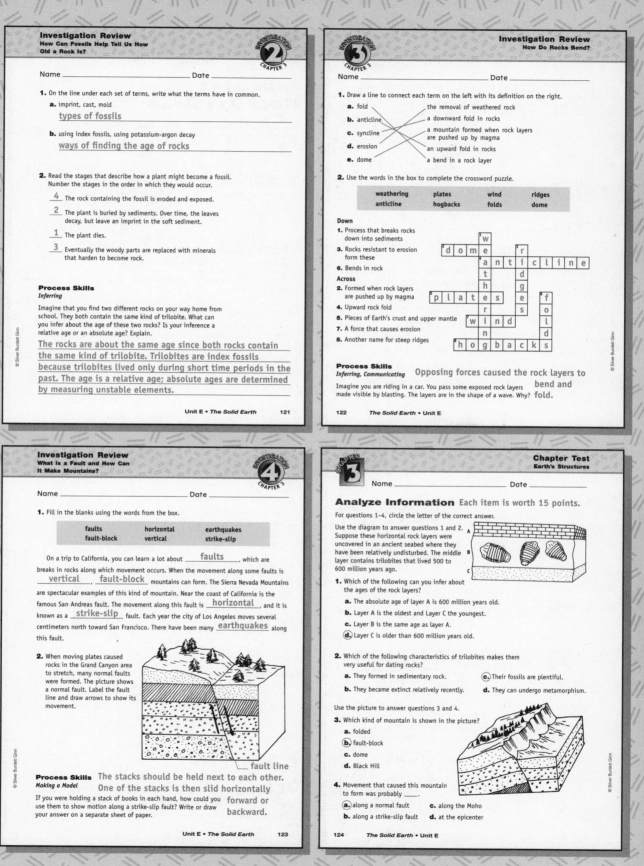

Investigation Review
How Can Fossils Help Tell Us How Old a Rock Is?

INVESTIGATION 2 CHAPTER 3

Name _____ Date _____

1. On the line under each set of terms, write what the terms have in common.

   a. imprint, cast, mold

   types of fossils

   b. using index fossils, using potassium-argon decay

   ways of finding the age of rocks

2. Read the stages that describe how a plant might become a fossil. Number the stages in the order in which they would occur.

   _4_ The rock containing the fossil is eroded and exposed.

   _2_ The plant is buried by sediments. Over time, the leaves decay, but leave an imprint in the soft sediment.

   _1_ The plant dies.

   _3_ Eventually the woody parts are replaced with minerals that harden to become rock.

Process Skills
Inferring

Imagine that you find two different rocks on your way home from school. They both contain the same kind of trilobite. What can you infer about the age of these two rocks? Is your inference a relative age or an absolute age? Explain.

The rocks are about the same age since both rocks contain the same kind of trilobite. Trilobites are index fossils because trilobites lived only during short time periods in the past. The age is a relative age; absolute ages are determined by measuring unstable elements.

Unit E • The Solid Earth   121

Investigation Review
How Do Rocks Bend?

INVESTIGATION 3 CHAPTER 3

Name _____ Date _____

1. Draw a line to connect each term on the left with its definition on the right.

   a. fold — the removal of weathered rock
   b. anticline — a downward fold in rocks
   c. syncline — a mountain formed when rock layers are pushed up by magma
   d. erosion — an upward fold in rocks
   e. dome — a bend in a rock layer

2. Use the words in the box to complete the crossword puzzle.

| weathering | plates | wind | ridges |
| anticline | hogbacks | folds | dome |

Down
1. Process that breaks rocks down into sediments
3. Rocks resistant to erosion form these
6. Bends in rock

Across
2. Formed when rock layers are pushed up by magma
4. Upward rock fold
5. Pieces of Earth's crust and upper mantle
7. A force that causes erosion
8. Another name for steep ridges

Crossword: dome, anticline, plates, wind, hogbacks (with weathering, ridges, folds down)

Process Skills
Inferring, Communicating   Opposing forces caused the rock layers to bend and fold.

Imagine you are riding in a car. You pass some exposed rock layers made visible by blasting. The layers are in the shape of a wave. Why?

122   The Solid Earth • Unit E

Investigation Review
What Is a Fault and How Can It Make Mountains?

INVESTIGATION 4 CHAPTER 3

Name _____ Date _____

1. Fill in the blanks using the words from the box.

| faults | horizontal | earthquakes |
| fault-block | vertical | strike-slip |

On a trip to California, you can learn a lot about __faults__, which are breaks in rocks along which movement occurs. When the movement along some faults is __vertical__, __fault-block__ mountains can form. The Sierra Nevada Mountains are spectacular examples of this kind of mountain. Near the coast of California is the famous San Andreas fault. The movement along this fault is __horizontal__, and it is known as a __strike-slip__ fault. Each year the city of Los Angeles moves several centimeters north toward San Francisco. There have been many __earthquakes__ along this fault.

2. When moving plates caused rocks in the Grand Canyon area to stretch, many normal faults were formed. The picture shows a normal fault. Label the fault line and draw arrows to show its movement.

fault line

Process Skills
Making a Model   The stacks should be held next to each other. One of the stacks is then slid horizontally forward or backward.

If you were holding a stack of books in each hand, how could you use them to show motion along a strike-slip fault? Write or draw your answer on a separate sheet of paper.

Unit E • The Solid Earth   123

CHAPTER 3

Chapter Test
Earth's Structures

Name _____ Date _____

Analyze Information   Each item is worth 15 points.

For questions 1–4, circle the letter of the correct answer.

Use the diagram to answer questions 1 and 2. Suppose these horizontal rock layers were uncovered in an ancient seabed where they have been relatively undisturbed. The middle layer contains trilobites that lived 500 to 600 million years ago.

1. Which of the following can you infer about the ages of the rock layers?
   a. The absolute age of layer A is 600 million years old.
   b. Layer A is the oldest and Layer C the youngest.
   c. Layer B is the same age as layer A.
   d. Layer C is older than 600 million years old.

2. Which of the following characteristics of trilobites makes them very useful for dating rocks?
   a. They formed in sedimentary rock.
   b. They became extinct relatively recently.
   c. Their fossils are plentiful.
   d. They can undergo metamorphism.

Use the picture to answer questions 3 and 4.

3. Which kind of mountain is shown in the picture?
   a. folded
   b. fault-block
   c. dome
   d. Black Hill

4. Movement that caused this mountain to form was probably ____.
   a. along a normal fault
   b. along a strike-slip fault
   c. along the Moho
   d. at the epicenter

124   The Solid Earth • Unit E

© Silver Burdett Ginn

205

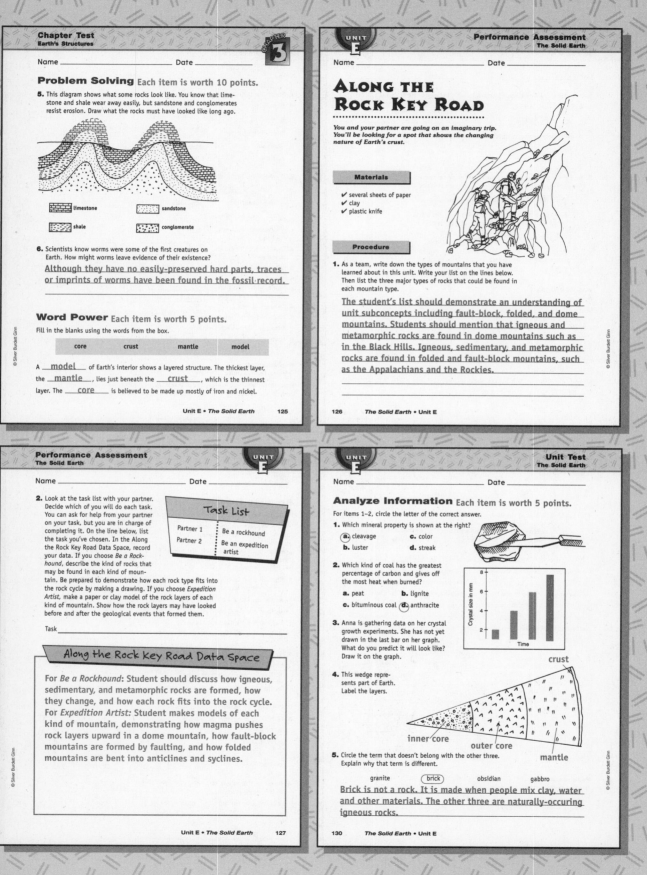

Chapter Test
Earth's Structures

3

Name _____ Date _____

Problem Solving Each item is worth 10 points.

5. This diagram shows what some rocks look like. You know that lime-stone and shale wear away easily, but sandstone and conglomerates resist erosion. Draw what the rocks must have looked like long ago.

- limestone
- shale
- sandstone
- conglomerate

6. Scientists know worms were some of the first creatures on Earth. How might worms leave evidence of their existence?

Although they have no easily-preserved hard parts, traces or imprints of worms have been found in the fossil record.

Word Power Each item is worth 5 points.

Fill in the blanks using the words from the box.

core	crust	mantle	model

A __model__ of Earth's interior shows a layered structure. The thickest layer, the __mantle__, lies just beneath the __crust__, which is the thinnest layer. The __core__ is believed to be made up mostly of iron and nickel.

Unit E • *The Solid Earth*   125

Performance Assessment
The Solid Earth

UNIT E

Name _____ Date _____

ALONG THE ROCK KEY ROAD

You and your partner are going on an imaginary trip. You'll be looking for a spot that shows the changing nature of Earth's crust.

Materials

✔ several sheets of paper
✔ clay
✔ plastic knife

Procedure

1. As a team, write down the types of mountains that you have learned about in this unit. Write your list on the lines below. Then list the three major types of rocks that could be found in each mountain type.

The student's list should demonstrate an understanding of unit subconcepts including fault-block, folded, and dome mountains. Students should mention that igneous and metamorphic rocks are found in dome mountains such as in the Black Hills. Igneous, sedimentary, and metamorphic rocks are found in folded and fault-block mountains, such as the Appalachians and the Rockies.

126   *The Solid Earth* • Unit E

Performance Assessment
The Solid Earth

UNIT E

Name _____ Date _____

2. Look at the task list with your partner. Decide which of you will do each task. You can ask for help from your partner on your task, but you are in charge of completing it. On the line below, list the task you've chosen. In the Along the Rock Key Road Data Space, record your data. If you choose *Be a Rock-hound*, describe the kind of rocks that may be found in each kind of mountain. Be prepared to demonstrate how each rock type fits into the rock cycle by making a drawing. If you choose *Expedition Artist*, make a paper or clay model of the rock layers of each kind of mountain. Show how the rock layers may have looked before and after the geological events that formed them.

Task List

| Partner 1 | Be a rockhound |
| Partner 2 | Be an expedition artist |

Task _____

Along the Rock Key Road Data Space

For *Be a Rockhound*: Student should discuss how igneous, sedimentary, and metamorphic rocks are formed, how they change, and how each rock fits into the rock cycle. For *Expedition Artist:* Student makes models of each kind of mountain, demonstrating how magma pushes rock layers upward in a dome mountain, how fault-block mountains are formed by faulting, and how folded mountains are bent into anticlines and syclines.

Unit E • *The Solid Earth*   127

Unit Test
The Solid Earth

UNIT E

Name _____ Date _____

Analyze Information Each item is worth 5 points.

For items 1–2, circle the letter of the correct answer.

1. Which mineral property is shown at the right?
- **a.** cleavage
- **b.** luster
- **c.** color
- **d.** streak

2. Which kind of coal has the greatest percentage of carbon and gives off the most heat when burned?
- **a.** peat
- **b.** lignite
- **c.** bituminous coal
- **d.** anthracite

3. Anna is gathering data on her crystal growth experiments. She has not yet drawn in the last bar on her graph. What do you predict it will look like? Draw it on the graph.

Crystal size in mm / Time

4. This wedge represents part of Earth. Label the layers.

crust
inner core
outer core
mantle

5. Circle the term that doesn't belong with the other three. Explain why that term is different.

granite   (brick)   obsidian   gabbro

Brick is not a rock. It is made when people mix clay, water and other materials. The other three are naturally-occuring igneous rocks.

130   *The Solid Earth* • Unit E

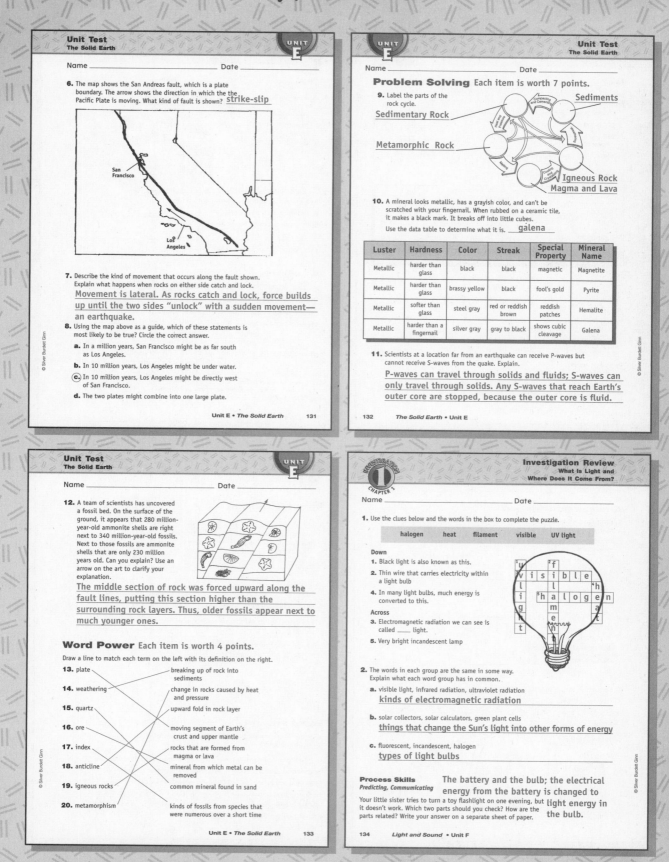

Unit Test
The Solid Earth

UNIT E

Name _____ Date _____

6. The map shows the San Andreas fault, which is a plate boundary. The arrow shows the direction in which the the Pacific Plate is moving. What kind of fault is shown? **strike-slip**

San Francisco

Los Angeles

7. Describe the kind of movement that occurs along the fault shown. Explain what happens when rocks on either side catch and lock.
   Movement is lateral. As rocks catch and lock, force builds up until the two sides "unlock" with a sudden movement—an earthquake.

8. Using the map above as a guide, which of these statements is most likely to be true? Circle the correct answer.
   a. In a million years, San Francisco might be as far south as Los Angeles.
   b. In 10 million years, Los Angeles might be under water.
   c. In 10 million years, Los Angeles might be directly west of San Francisco.
   d. The two plates might combine into one large plate.

© Silver Burdett Ginn

Unit E • The Solid Earth   131

UNIT E

Unit Test
The Solid Earth

Name _____ Date _____

Problem Solving Each item is worth 7 points.

9. Label the parts of the rock cycle.

   Sedimentary Rock

   Metamorphic Rock

   Compacting and Cementing

   Sediments

   Igneous Rock
   Magma and Lava

10. A mineral looks metallic, has a grayish color, and can't be scratched with your fingernail. When rubbed on a ceramic tile, it makes a black mark. It breaks off into little cubes.
    Use the data table to determine what it is. **galena**

Luster	Hardness	Color	Streak	Special Property	Mineral Name
Metallic	harder than glass	black	black	magnetic	Magnetite
Metallic	harder than glass	brassy yellow	black	fool's gold	Pyrite
Metallic	softer than glass	steel gray	red or reddish brown	reddish patches	Hematite
Metallic	harder than a fingernail	silver gray	gray to black	shows cubic cleavage	Galena

11. Scientists at a location far from an earthquake can receive P-waves but cannot receive S-waves from the quake. Explain.
    P-waves can travel through solids and fluids; S-waves can only travel through solids. Any S-waves that reach Earth's outer core are stopped, because the outer core is fluid.

© Silver Burdett Ginn

132   The Solid Earth • Unit E

Unit Test
The Solid Earth

UNIT E

Name _____ Date _____

12. A team of scientists has uncovered a fossil bed. On the surface of the ground, it appears that 280 million-year-old ammonite shells are right next to 340 million-year-old fossils. Next to those fossils are ammonite shells that are only 230 million years old. Can you explain? Use an arrow on the art to clarify your explanation.
    The middle section of rock was forced upward along the fault lines, putting this section higher than the surrounding rock layers. Thus, older fossils appear next to much younger ones.

Word Power Each item is worth 4 points.

Draw a line to match each term on the left with its definition on the right.

13. plate — breaking up of rock into sediments
14. weathering — change in rocks caused by heat and pressure
15. quartz — upward fold in rock layer
16. ore — moving segment of Earth's crust and upper mantle
17. index — rocks that are formed from magma or lava
18. anticline — mineral from which metal can be removed
19. igneous rocks — common mineral found in sand
20. metamorphism — kinds of fossils from species that were numerous over a short time

© Silver Burdett Ginn

Unit E • The Solid Earth   133

INVESTIGATION 1
CHAPTER 1

Investigation Review
What Is Light and Where Does It Come From?

Name _____ Date _____

1. Use the clues below and the words in the box to complete the puzzle.

   | halogen | heat | filament | visible | UV light |

   Down
   1. Black light is also known as this.
   2. Thin wire that carries electricity within a light bulb
   4. In many light bulbs, much energy is converted to this.

   Across
   3. Electromagnetic radiation we can see is called _____ light.
   5. Very bright incandescent lamp

   Crossword: u-v-l-i-g-h-t (down), f-i-l-a-m-e-n-t, visible, halogen, heat

2. The words in each group are the same in some way. Explain what each word group has in common.
   a. visible light, infrared radiation, ultraviolet radiation
      kinds of electromagnetic radiation
   b. solar collectors, solar calculators, green plant cells
      things that change the Sun's light into other forms of energy
   c. fluorescent, incandescent, halogen
      types of light bulbs

Process Skills
Predicting, Communicating
Your little sister tries to turn a toy flashlight on one evening, but it doesn't work. Which two parts should you check? How are the parts related? Write your answer on a separate sheet of paper.
The battery and the bulb; the electrical energy from the battery is changed to light energy in the bulb.

© Silver Burdett Ginn

134   Light and Sound • Unit F

Answers

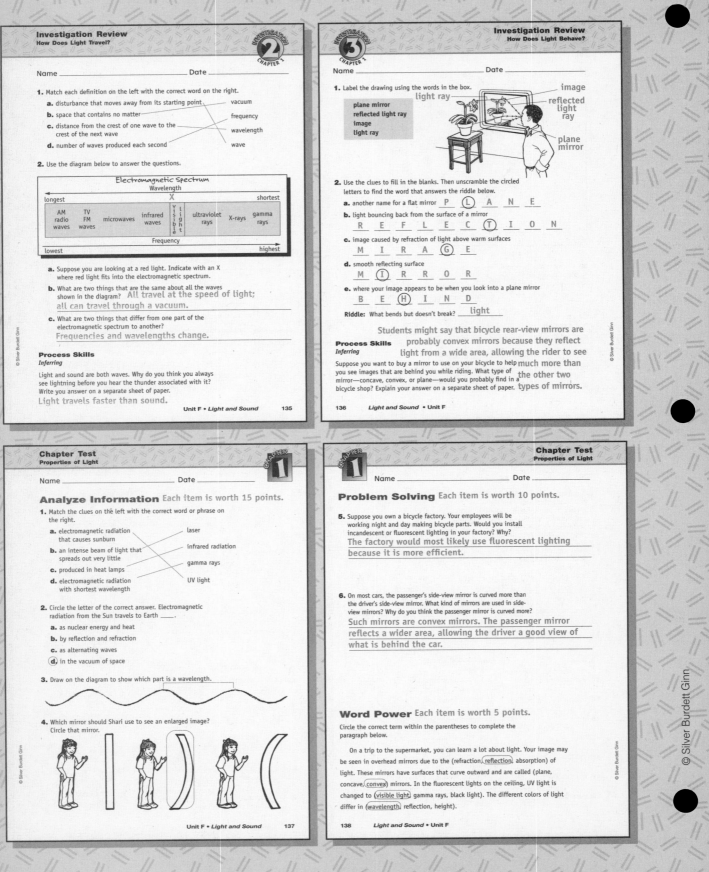

Investigation Review
How Does Light Travel?

INVESTIGATION 2 CHAPTER 1

Name _____ Date _____

1. Match each definition on the left with the correct word on the right.

   a. disturbance that moves away from its starting point — vacuum

   b. space that contains no matter — frequency

   c. distance from the crest of one wave to the crest of the next wave — wavelength

   d. number of waves produced each second — wave

2. Use the diagram below to answer the questions.

Electromagnetic Spectrum

Wavelength								
longest				X				shortest
AM radio waves	TV FM waves	microwaves	infrared waves	visible light	ultraviolet rays	X-rays	gamma rays	
lowest				Frequency				highest

   a. Suppose you are looking at a red light. Indicate with an X where red light fits into the electromagnetic spectrum.

   b. What are two things that are the same about all the waves shown in the diagram? **All travel at the speed of light; all can travel through a vacuum.**

   c. What are two things that differ from one part of the electromagnetic spectrum to another? **Frequencies and wavelengths change.**

Process Skills
Inferring

Light and sound are both waves. Why do you think you always see lightning before you hear the thunder associated with it? Write you answer on a separate sheet of paper.
Light travels faster than sound.

Unit F • Light and Sound   135

Investigation Review
How Does Light Behave?

INVESTIGATION 3 CHAPTER 1

Name _____ Date _____

1. Label the drawing using the words in the box.

   plane mirror
   reflected light ray
   image
   light ray

   image
   light ray
   reflected light ray
   plane mirror

2. Use the clues to fill in the blanks. Then unscramble the circled letters to find the word that answers the riddle below.

   a. another name for a flat mirror P L A N E

   b. light bouncing back from the surface of a mirror R E F L E C T I O N

   c. image caused by refraction of light above warm surfaces M I R A G E

   d. smooth reflecting surface M I R R O R

   e. where your image appears to be when you look into a plane mirror B E H I N D

   Riddle: What bends but doesn't break? _____light_____

Process Skills
Inferring

Suppose you want to buy a mirror to use on your bicycle to help you see images that are behind you while riding. What type of mirror—concave, convex, or plane—would you probably find in a bicycle shop? Explain your answer on a separate sheet of paper.

Students might say that bicycle rear-view mirrors are probably convex mirrors because they reflect light from a wide area, allowing the rider to see much more than the other two types of mirrors.

136   Light and Sound • Unit F

Chapter Test
Properties of Light

CHAPTER 1

Name _____ Date _____

Analyze Information Each item is worth 15 points.

1. Match the clues on the left with the correct word or phrase on the right.

   a. electromagnetic radiation that causes sunburn — laser

   b. an intense beam of light that spreads out very little — infrared radiation

   c. produced in heat lamps — gamma rays

   d. electromagnetic radiation with shortest wavelength — UV light

2. Circle the letter of the correct answer. Electromagnetic radiation from the Sun travels to Earth ____ .

   a. as nuclear energy and heat

   b. by reflection and refraction

   c. as alternating waves

   (d.) in the vacuum of space

3. Draw on the diagram to show which part is a wavelength.

4. Which mirror should Shari use to see an enlarged image? Circle that mirror.

Unit F • Light and Sound   137

Chapter Test
Properties of Light

CHAPTER 1

Name _____ Date _____

Problem Solving Each item is worth 10 points.

5. Suppose you own a bicycle factory. Your employees will be working night and day making bicycle parts. Would you install incandescent or fluorescent lighting in your factory? Why?
The factory would most likely use fluorescent lighting because it is more efficient.

6. On most cars, the passenger's side-view mirror is curved more than the driver's side-view mirror. What kind of mirrors are used in side-view mirrors? Why do you think the passenger mirror is curved more?
Such mirrors are convex mirrors. The passenger mirror reflects a wider area, allowing the driver a good view of what is behind the car.

Word Power Each item is worth 5 points.

Circle the correct term within the parentheses to complete the paragraph below.

On a trip to the supermarket, you can learn a lot about light. Your image may be seen in overhead mirrors due to the (refraction, (reflection), absorption) of light. These mirrors have surfaces that curve outward and are called (plane, concave, (convex)) mirrors. In the fluorescent lights on the ceiling, UV light is changed to ((visible light), gamma rays, black light). The different colors of light differ in ((wavelength), reflection, height).

138   Light and Sound • Unit F

© Silver Burdett Ginn

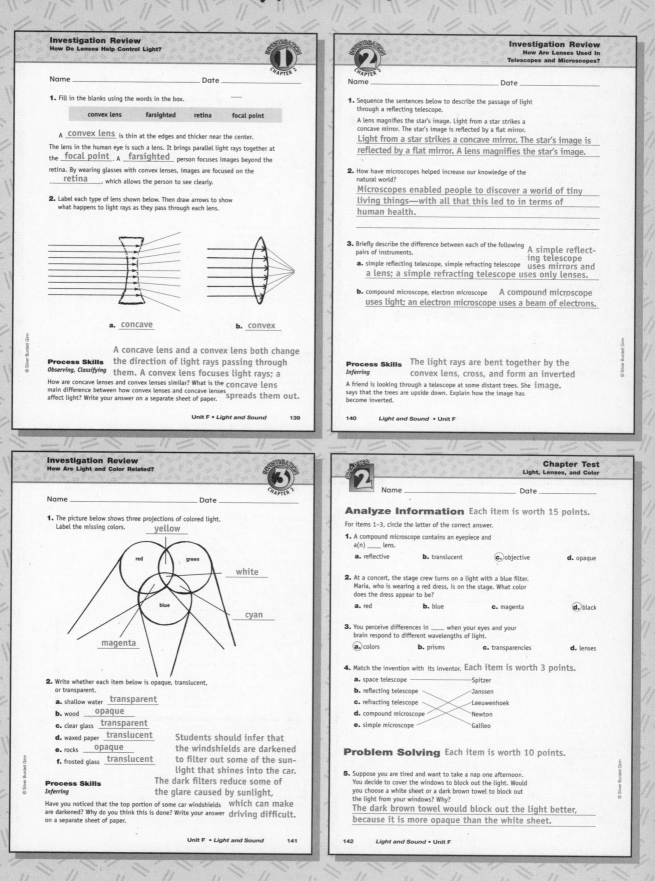

Investigation Review
How Do Lenses Help Control Light?

INVESTIGATION 1 CHAPTER 2

Name _____ Date _____

1. Fill in the blanks using the words in the box.

| convex lens | farsighted | retina | focal point |

A __convex lens__ is thin at the edges and thicker near the center.
The lens in the human eye is such a lens. It brings parallel light rays together at
the __focal point__ . A __farsighted__ person focuses images beyond the
retina. By wearing glasses with convex lenses, images are focused on the
__retina__ , which allows the person to see clearly.

2. Label each type of lens shown below. Then draw arrows to show
what happens to light rays as they pass through each lens.

a. __concave__   b. __convex__

Process Skills
Observing, Classifying

How are concave lenses and convex lenses similar? What is the
main difference between how convex lenses and concave lenses
affect light? Write your answer on a separate sheet of paper.

A concave lens and a convex lens both change
the direction of light rays passing through
them. A convex lens focuses light rays; a
concave lens
spreads them out.

Unit F • *Light and Sound*   139

Investigation Review
How Are Lenses Used In Telescopes and Microscopes?

INVESTIGATION 2 CHAPTER 2

Name _____ Date _____

1. Sequence the sentences below to describe the passage of light
through a reflecting telescope.

A lens magnifies the star's image. Light from a star strikes a
concave mirror. The star's image is reflected by a flat mirror.

__Light from a star strikes a concave mirror. The star's image is
reflected by a flat mirror. A lens magnifies the star's image.__

2. How have microscopes helped increase our knowledge of the
natural world?
__Microscopes enabled people to discover a world of tiny
living things—with all that this led to in terms of
human health.__

3. Briefly describe the difference between each of the following
pairs of instruments.
a. simple reflecting telescope, simple refracting telescope

__A simple reflecting telescope uses mirrors and
a lens; a simple refracting telescope uses only lenses.__

b. compound microscope, electron microscope __A compound microscope
uses light; an electron microscope uses a beam of electrons.__

Process Skills
Inferring

A friend is looking through a telescope at some distant trees. She
says that the trees are upside down. Explain how the image has
become inverted.

The light rays are bent together by the
convex lens, cross, and form an inverted
image.

140   *Light and Sound* • Unit F

Investigation Review
How Are Light and Color Related?

INVESTIGATION 3 CHAPTER 2

Name _____ Date _____

1. The picture below shows three projections of colored light.
Label the missing colors.

yellow

red   green

white

blue

cyan

magenta

2. Write whether each item below is opaque, translucent,
or transparent.
a. shallow water __transparent__
b. wood __opaque__
c. clear glass __transparent__
d. waxed paper __translucent__
e. rocks __opaque__
f. frosted glass __translucent__

Process Skills
Inferring

Have you noticed that the top portion of some car windshields
are darkened? Why do you think this is done? Write your answer
on a separate sheet of paper.

Students should infer that
the windshields are darkened
to filter out some of the sunlight that shines into the car.
The dark filters reduce some of
the glare caused by sunlight,
which can make
driving difficult.

Unit F • *Light and Sound*   141

Chapter Test
Light, Lenses, and Color

CHAPTER 2

Name _____ Date _____

Analyze Information   Each item is worth 15 points.

For items 1–3, circle the letter of the correct answer.

1. A compound microscope contains an eyepiece and
a(n) _____ lens.
a. reflective   b. translucent   c. objective   d. opaque

2. At a concert, the stage crew turns on a light with a blue filter.
Maria, who is wearing a red dress, is on the stage. What color
does the dress appear to be?
a. red   b. blue   c. magenta   d. black

3. You perceive differences in _____ when your eyes and your
brain respond to different wavelengths of light.
a. colors   b. prisms   c. transparencies   d. lenses

4. Match the invention with its inventor. Each item is worth 3 points.
a. space telescope ——————— Spitzer
b. reflecting telescope ——— Janssen
c. refracting telescope ——— Leeuwenhoek
d. compound microscope ——— Newton
e. simple microscope ——— Galileo

Problem Solving   Each item is worth 10 points.

5. Suppose you are tired and want to take a nap one afternoon.
You decide to cover the windows to block out the light. Would
you choose a white sheet or a dark brown towel to block out
the light from your windows? Why?
__The dark brown towel would block out the light better,
because it is more opaque than the white sheet.__

142   *Light and Sound* • Unit F

© Silver Burdett Ginn

209

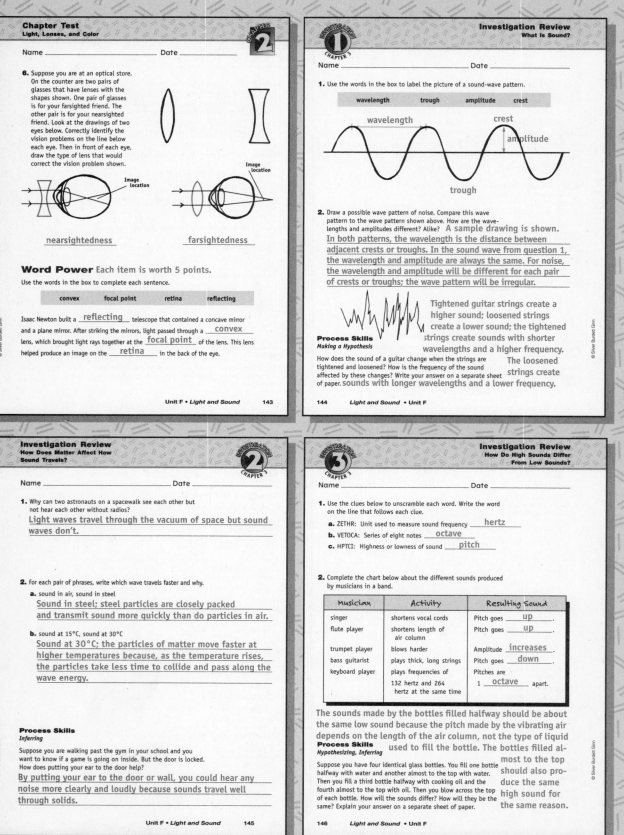

Answers

Chapter Test
Light, Lenses, and Color

CHAPTER 2

Name _____ Date _____

6. Suppose you are at an optical store. On the counter are two pairs of glasses that have lenses with the shapes shown. One pair of glasses is for your farsighted friend. The other pair is for your nearsighted friend. Look at the drawings of two eyes below. Correctly identify the vision problems on the line below each eye. Then in front of each eye, draw the type of lens that would correct the vision problem shown.

Image location

Image location

nearsightedness   farsightedness

Word Power Each item is worth 5 points.

Use the words in the box to complete each sentence.

convex	focal point	retina	reflecting

Isaac Newton built a __reflecting__ telescope that contained a concave mirror and a plane mirror. After striking the mirrors, light passed through a __convex__ lens, which brought light rays together at the __focal point__ of the lens. This lens helped produce an image on the __retina__ in the back of the eye.

Unit F • Light and Sound   143

Investigation Review
What Is Sound?

INVESTIGATION 1 CHAPTER 3

Name _____ Date _____

1. Use the words in the box to label the picture of a sound-wave pattern.

wavelength	trough	amplitude	crest

wavelength   crest

amplitude

trough

2. Draw a possible wave pattern of noise. Compare this wave pattern to the wave pattern shown above. How are the wavelengths and amplitudes different? Alike? A sample drawing is shown. In both patterns, the wavelength is the distance between adjacent crests or troughs. In the sound wave from question 1, the wavelength and amplitude are always the same. For noise, the wavelength and amplitude will be different for each pair of crests or troughs; the wave pattern will be irregular.

Process Skills
Making a Hypothesis

How does the sound of a guitar change when the strings are tightened and loosened? How is the frequency of the sound affected by these changes? Write your answer on a separate sheet of paper. Tightened guitar strings create a higher sound; loosened strings create a lower sound; the tightened strings create sounds with shorter wavelengths and a higher frequency. The loosened strings create sounds with longer wavelengths and a lower frequency.

144   *Light and Sound* • Unit F

Investigation Review
How Does Matter Affect How Sound Travels?

INVESTIGATION 2 CHAPTER 3

Name _____ Date _____

1. Why can two astronauts on a spacewalk see each other but not hear each other without radios?
Light waves travel through the vacuum of space but sound waves don't.

2. For each pair of phrases, write which wave travels faster and why.

a. sound in air, sound in steel
Sound in steel; steel particles are closely packed and transmit sound more quickly than do particles in air.

b. sound at 15°C, sound at 30°C
Sound at 30°C; the particles of matter move faster at higher temperatures because, as the temperature rises, the particles take less time to collide and pass along the wave energy.

Process Skills
Inferring

Suppose you are walking past the gym in your school and you want to know if a game is going on inside. But the door is locked. How does putting your ear to the door help?
By putting your ear to the door or wall, you could hear any noise more clearly and loudly because sounds travel well through solids.

Unit F • Light and Sound   145

Investigation Review
How Do High Sounds Differ From Low Sounds?

INVESTIGATION 3 CHAPTER 3

Name _____ Date _____

1. Use the clues below to unscramble each word. Write the word on the line that follows each clue.

a. ZETHR: Unit used to measure sound frequency __hertz__

b. VETOCA: Series of eight notes __octave__

c. HPTCI: Highness or lowness of sound __pitch__

2. Complete the chart below about the different sounds produced by musicians in a band.

Musician	Activity	Resulting Sound
singer	shortens vocal cords	Pitch goes __up__.
flute player	shortens length of air column	Pitch goes __up__.
trumpet player	blows harder	Amplitude __increases__.
bass guitarist	plays thick, long strings	Pitch goes __down__.
keyboard player	plays frequencies of 132 hertz and 264 hertz at the same time	Pitches are 1 __octave__ apart.

Process Skills
Hypothesizing, Inferring

Suppose you have four identical glass bottles. You fill one bottle halfway with water and another almost to the top with water. Then you fill a third bottle halfway with cooking oil and the fourth almost to the top with oil. Then you blow across the tops of each bottle. How will the sounds differ? How will they be the same? Explain your answer on a separate sheet of paper. The sounds made by the bottles filled halfway should be about the same low sound because the pitch made by the vibrating air depends on the length of the air column, not the type of liquid used to fill the bottle. The bottles filled almost to the top should also produce the same high sound for the same reason.

146   *Light and Sound* • Unit F

© Silver Burdett Ginn

210

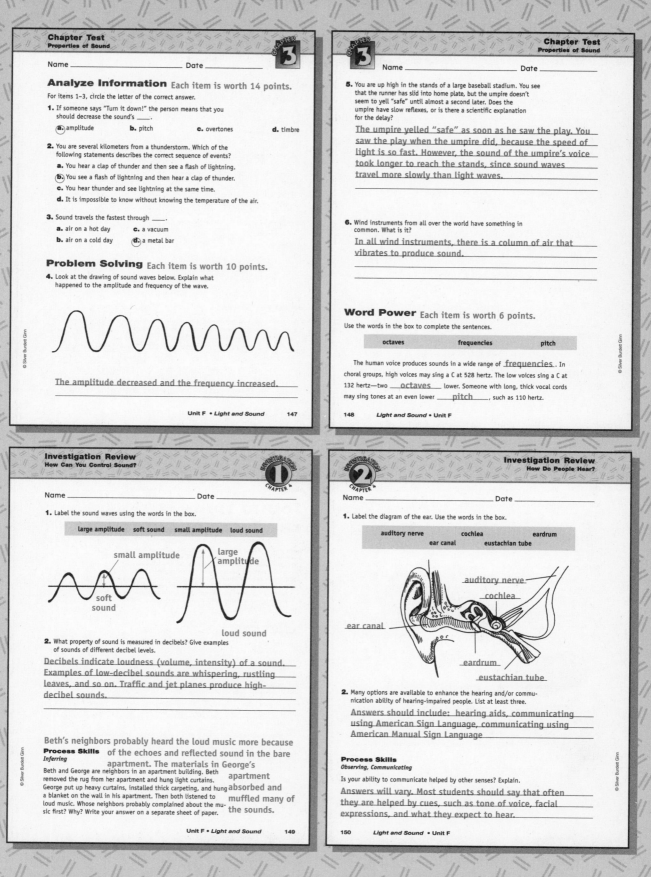

Chapter Test
Properties of Sound

CHAPTER 3

Name _____ Date _____

Analyze Information Each item is worth 14 points.

For items 1–3, circle the letter of the correct answer.

1. If someone says "Turn it down!" the person means that you should decrease the sound's _____.

   a. amplitude (circled)   b. pitch   c. overtones   d. timbre

2. You are several kilometers from a thunderstorm. Which of the following statements describes the correct sequence of events?

   a. You hear a clap of thunder and then see a flash of lightning.

   b. You see a flash of lightning and then hear a clap of thunder. (circled)

   c. You hear thunder and see lightning at the same time.

   d. It is impossible to know without knowing the temperature of the air.

3. Sound travels the fastest through _____.

   a. air on a hot day   c. a vacuum

   b. air on a cold day   **d. a metal bar** (circled)

Problem Solving Each item is worth 10 points.

4. Look at the drawing of sound waves below. Explain what happened to the amplitude and frequency of the wave.

   <u>The amplitude decreased and the frequency increased.</u>

CHAPTER 3

Chapter Test
Properties of Sound

Name _____ Date _____

5. You are up high in the stands of a large baseball stadium. You see that the runner has slid into home plate, but the umpire doesn't seem to yell "safe" until almost a second later. Does the umpire have slow reflexes, or is there a scientific explanation for the delay?

   <u>The umpire yelled "safe" as soon as he saw the play. You saw the play when the umpire did, because the speed of light is so fast. However, the sound of the umpire's voice took longer to reach the stands, since sound waves travel more slowly than light waves.</u>

6. Wind instruments from all over the world have something in common. What is it?

   <u>In all wind instruments, there is a column of air that vibrates to produce sound.</u>

Word Power Each item is worth 6 points.

Use the words in the box to complete the sentences.

octaves	frequencies	pitch

The human voice produces sounds in a wide range of <u>frequencies</u>. In choral groups, high voices may sing a C at 528 hertz. The low voices sing a C at 132 hertz—two <u>octaves</u> lower. Someone with long, thick vocal cords may sing tones at an even lower <u>pitch</u>, such as 110 hertz.

Investigation Review
How Can You Control Sound?

INVESTIGATION 1 CHAPTER 4

Name _____ Date _____

1. Label the sound waves using the words in the box.

large amplitude	soft sound	small amplitude	loud sound

   small amplitude
   soft sound
   large amplitude
   loud sound

2. What property of sound is measured in decibels? Give examples of sounds of different decibel levels.

   <u>Decibels indicate loudness (volume, intensity) of a sound. Examples of low-decibel sounds are whispering, rustling leaves, and so on. Traffic and jet planes produce high-decibel sounds.</u>

Process Skills
Inferring

Beth and George are neighbors in an apartment building. Beth removed the rug from her apartment and hung light curtains. George put up heavy curtains, installed thick carpeting, and hung a blanket on the wall in his apartment. Then both listened to loud music. Whose neighbors probably complained about the music first? Why? Write your answer on a separate sheet of paper.

<u>Beth's neighbors probably heard the loud music more because of the echoes and reflected sound in the bare apartment. The materials in George's apartment absorbed and muffled many of the sounds.</u>

INVESTIGATION 2 CHAPTER 4

Investigation Review
How Do People Hear?

Name _____ Date _____

1. Label the diagram of the ear. Use the words in the box.

auditory nerve	cochlea	eardrum
ear canal	eustachian tube	

   auditory nerve
   cochlea
   ear canal
   eardrum
   eustachian tube

2. Many options are available to enhance the hearing and/or communication ability of hearing-impaired people. List at least three.

   <u>Answers should include: hearing aids, communicating using American Sign Language, communicating using American Manual Sign Language</u>

Process Skills
Observing, Communicating

Is your ability to communicate helped by other senses? Explain.

<u>Answers will vary. Most students should say that often they are helped by cues, such as tone of voice, facial expressions, and what they expect to hear.</u>

Answers

Investigation Review
How Is Sound Transmitted and Recorded?

Name _____ Date _____

INVESTIGATION 3 CHAPTER 4

1. Draw a line connecting the recording device on the right to its characteristics on the left.

   a. A laser reads a series of pits and flat areas that represent electric signals. — phonograph record

   b. The magnetic field of tiny crystals of iron oxide respond to changing electric signals. — CD

   c. A stylus vibrates as it moves over the tiny hills and valleys of a spiral track. — audiocassettes

2. Number these items in order from 1 to 5 to show the history of recording sound. 1 = oldest; 5 = newest.

   _5_ CDs

   _3_ long-playing records

   _1_ Edison's phonograph

   _2_ Berliner's masters

   _4_ audiocassette tape

Process Skills
Inferring

You leave some of your favorite audiocassettes in the science laboratory near a powerful magnet belonging to the teacher. You later find that your tapes are distorted. What happened?
The magnet erased or affected the magnetic patterns stored on the tapes.

Unit F • *Light and Sound*   151

Chapter Test
Hearing and Recording Sound

CHAPTER 4

Name _____ Date _____

Analyzing Information Each item is worth 14 points.
For items 1–3, circle the letter of the correct answer.

1. A stylus and cartridge are parts of which sound device?
   - **a.** phonograph
   - b. audiocassette
   - c. CD
   - d. hearing aid

2. Which of the following materials would be the best flooring to use to absorb sound?
   - a. concrete
   - **c.** carpeting
   - b. tile
   - d. wood

3. The sound having the highest decibel level is ____.
   - a. heavy traffic
   - b. whispering
   - c. thunder
   - **d.** nearby rocket taking off

Problem Solving Each item is worth 10 points.

4. The information superhighway provides people with many advantages. Describe three advantages of using the information superhighway and one disadvantage of using it.
   Positive aspects might include availability of information through libraries and databases and communicating with other users. Disadvantages might include a decrease in the amount of time people communicate in person and the possibility of information being misused. Answers will vary.

152   *Light and Sound* • Unit F

Chapter Test
Hearing and Recording Sound

CHAPTER 4

Name _____ Date _____

5. Why does swallowing when you are in an airplane help to relieve the pressure in your ears?
   Swallowing helps to equalize the air pressure on both sides of your eardrum.

6. Explain how a hearing aid can help a person with a hearing loss.
   A hearing aid receives sound waves, converts them to electrical signals, amplifies the signals, and converts them back to sound waves to help a person hear.

Word Power Each item is worth 7 points.

Fill in the blanks using the words from the box.

| compact disc | volume | decibels | auditory nerve |

To play a _compact disc_, a laser reads pits and flat areas and produces a digital code. The _volume_ of the sound waves produced from the coded signal is measured in _decibels_. In your ear, vibrations caused by sound waves travel to your _auditory nerve_ and then into your brain. Then you hear your favorite song.

Unit F • *Light and Sound*   153

Performance Assessment
Light and Sound

UNIT F

Name _____ Date _____

SOUND IDEAS AT THE SPEED OF LIGHT

Have you ever heard the expression "Now you see it, now you don't"? You and your partner will write riddles or draw pictures to explain some important ideas about sound. Part of the task will be to choose colored markers and cellophane that will "hide" the answers or some part of the picture. When the cellophane is lifted, your message shows in a flash! If you have worked on any musical instruments for the unit project, bring them in for sound effects while you show your cards.

Materials

- ✔ colored markers
- ✔ index cards
- ✔ colored cellophane
- ✔ tape

Procedure

1. In the Data Space on page 155, answer the questions below. Then you and your partner will make a set of cards with riddles about each question.
   - **a.** How does light travel?
   - **b.** What happens to light when it goes through a lens? Strikes a mirror?
   - **c.** How does sound travel through different materials?
   - **d.** What are the characteristics of musical sounds?
   - **e.** What are some ways that sound is recorded?

   After you have written your answers, decide on the color combinations of markers and cellophane you will use for each card. Record them in the Data Space. Remember that you will write some information so that it can be read through the cellophane and some information so that it will be hidden by the cellophane.

154   *Light and Sound* • Unit F

·············· Answers ··············

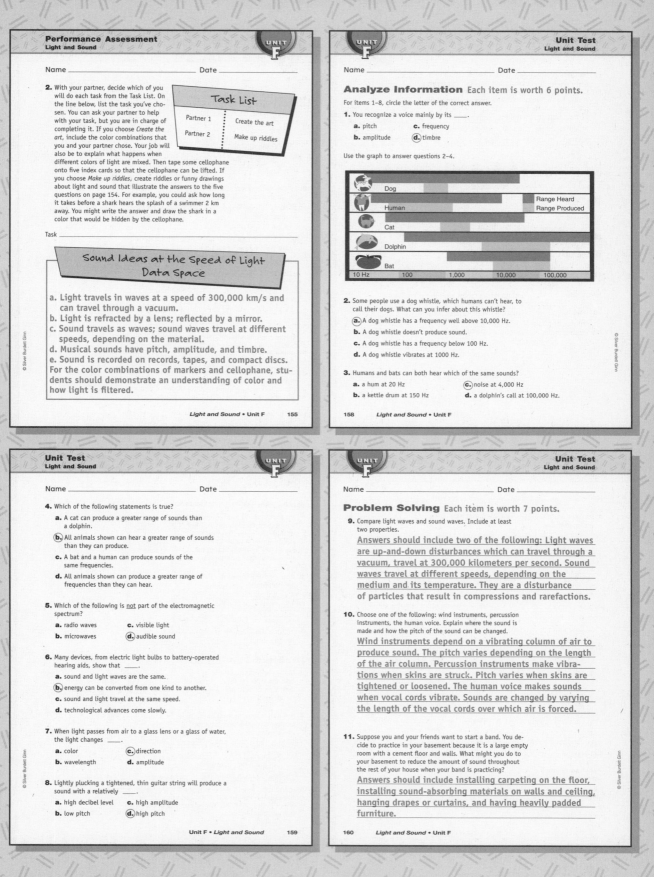

Performance Assessment
Light and Sound

UNIT F

Name _____ Date _____

2. With your partner, decide which of you will do each task from the Task List. On the line below, list the task you've chosen. You can ask your partner to help with your task, but you are in charge of completing it. If you choose *Create the art*, include the color combinations that you and your partner chose. Your job will also be to explain what happens when different colors of light are mixed. Then tape some cellophane onto five index cards so that the cellophane can be lifted. If you choose *Make up riddles*, create riddles or funny drawings about light and sound that illustrate the answers to the five questions on page 154. For example, you could ask how long it takes before a shark hears the splash of a swimmer 2 km away. You might write the answer and draw the shark in a color that would be hidden by the cellophane.

Task List

Partner 1 ⋯⋯ Create the art

Partner 2 ⋯⋯ Make up riddles

Task _____

Sound Ideas at the Speed of Light
Data Space

a. Light travels in waves at a speed of 300,000 km/s and can travel through a vacuum.
b. Light is refracted by a lens; reflected by a mirror.
c. Sound travels as waves; sound waves travel at different speeds, depending on the material.
d. Musical sounds have pitch, amplitude, and timbre.
e. Sound is recorded on records, tapes, and compact discs.
For the color combinations of markers and cellophane, students should demonstrate an understanding of color and how light is filtered.

Light and Sound • Unit F 155

UNIT F

Unit Test
Light and Sound

Name _____ Date _____

Analyze Information Each item is worth 6 points.

For items 1–8, circle the letter of the correct answer.

1. You recognize a voice mainly by its ____.
a. pitch   c. frequency
b. amplitude   (d.) timbre

Use the graph to answer questions 2–4.

		Range Heard
Dog		
Human		Range Produced
Cat		
Dolphin		
Bat		
10 Hz 100 1,000 10,000 100,000		

2. Some people use a dog whistle, which humans can't hear, to call their dogs. What can you infer about this whistle?
(a.) A dog whistle has a frequency well above 10,000 Hz.
b. A dog whistle doesn't produce sound.
c. A dog whistle has a frequency below 100 Hz.
d. A dog whistle vibrates at 1000 Hz.

3. Humans and bats can both hear which of the same sounds?
a. a hum at 20 Hz   (c.) noise at 4,000 Hz
b. a kettle drum at 150 Hz   d. a dolphin's call at 100,000 Hz.

158   *Light and Sound • Unit F*

Unit Test
Light and Sound

UNIT F

Name _____ Date _____

4. Which of the following statements is true?
a. A cat can produce a greater range of sounds than a dolphin.
(b.) All animals shown can hear a greater range of sounds than they can produce.
c. A bat and a human can produce sounds of the same frequencies.
d. All animals shown can produce a greater range of frequencies than they can hear.

5. Which of the following is not part of the electromagnetic spectrum?
a. radio waves   c. visible light
b. microwaves   (d.) audible sound

6. Many devices, from electric light bulbs to battery-operated hearing aids, show that ____.
a. sound and light waves are the same.
(b.) energy can be converted from one kind to another.
c. sound and light travel at the same speed.
d. technological advances come slowly.

7. When light passes from air to a glass lens or a glass of water, the light changes ____.
a. color   (c.) direction
b. wavelength   d. amplitude

8. Lightly plucking a tightened, thin guitar string will produce a sound with a relatively ____.
a. high decibel level   c. high amplitude
b. low pitch   (d.) high pitch

Unit F • Light and Sound 159

UNIT F

Unit Test
Light and Sound

Name _____ Date _____

Problem Solving Each item is worth 7 points.

9. Compare light waves and sound waves. Include at least two properties.
Answers should include two of the following: Light waves are up-and-down disturbances which can travel through a vacuum, travel at 300,000 kilometers per second. Sound waves travel at different speeds, depending on the medium and its temperature. They are a disturbance of particles that result in compressions and rarefactions.

10. Choose one of the following: wind instruments, percussion instruments, the human voice. Explain where the sound is made and how the pitch of the sound can be changed.
Wind instruments depend on a vibrating column of air to produce sound. The pitch varies depending on the length of the air column. Percussion instruments make vibrations when skins are struck. Pitch varies when skins are tightened or loosened. The human voice makes sounds when vocal cords vibrate. Sounds are changed by varying the length of the vocal cords over which air is forced.

11. Suppose you and your friends want to start a band. You decide to practice in your basement because it is a large empty room with a cement floor and walls. What might you do to your basement to reduce the amount of sound throughout the rest of your house when your band is practicing?
Answers should include installing carpeting on the floor, installing sound-absorbing materials on walls and ceiling, hanging drapes or curtains, and having heavily padded furniture.

160   *Light and Sound • Unit F*

Answers

Unit Test
Light and Sound

UNIT F

12. Suppose your digital watch alarm is broken and you can't turn it off. The sound is really bothering you. Your friend suggests that you wrap the watch in a cloth and put it in a wooden box, but you can still hear the alarm. Why are you still able to hear the sound?
Sound waves travel through matter. The sound was still able to travel through the cloth and through the wood and the air in the box, so you could still hear it.

Word Power Each item is worth 3 points.

Match each term on the left with the correct definition on the right.

13. frequency ———— number of waves produced each second

14. concave — measure of sound intensity

15. timbre — distance from a point on one wave to the same point on the next wave

16. refraction — bending of light

17. translucent — quality of a sound

18. decibel — lens that is thicker at the edges than at the center

19. reflection — allowing some light to pass through it

20. wavelength — bouncing of light from a surface

© Silver Burdett Ginn

Investigation Review
What Are the Parts of the Skeletal System?

INVESTIGATION 1 CHAPTER 1

Name _____ Date _____

1. The terms in the box are different kinds of joints. Match each part of the body in the drawing with the kind of joint that helps it move.

pivot joint
ball-and-socket joint
hinge joint
gliding joint

ball-and-socket joint
hinge joint
pivot joint
gliding joint

2. Use the clues below to unscramble each word. Then use the circled letters to find the answer to the riddle below.

a. Strong bands of fiber that hold bones in place and allow some movement:
MEATLINGS   l i g a m e (n) t s

b. Places where bones come together but allow no movement:
BAMOLIVEM TINJOS
i m m o v a b l e   (j) o i n t s

c. Tissue that is similar to bone but is more flexible:
GILRATACE   c a r t (i) l a g e

d. What the ribs do for the heart, lungs, and soft organs:
RETTOCP   p r (o) t e c t

e. The middle part of a long bone: THAFS   s h a f (t)

Riddle: Where is the favorite place for bones to meet each other? _____ joint

Process Skills
Making and Using Models

Suppose you want to make a model of the bones and immovable joints in the skull. You have a plastic-foam ball and some modeling clay to work with. On a separate sheet of paper, draw or write how you would show how the bones of the skull protect the brain.
The ball could represent the brain. Students could roll the clay into thin sheets and cut them to fit around the ball to represent how the bones of the skull protect the brain.

© Silver Burdett Ginn

Investigation Review
How Do Bones and Muscles Cause Movement?

INVESTIGATION 2 CHAPTER 1

Name _____ Date _____

1. Use the words in the box to complete the sentences in the paragraph below.

| arm | bend | biceps |
| relaxes | pairs | triceps |

Skeletal muscles work in **pairs** to move parts of your body. The **biceps** and triceps in your arm work like a team. When the biceps contracts, the **triceps** muscle stretches and relaxes. These movements make your arm **bend** at the elbow. When the triceps contracts, the other muscle of the pair **relaxes**. That straightens your **arm**.

2. Write the missing words.

kinds of muscle

a. **Skeletal** muscles move bones.

b. **Smooth** muscles are found in the stomach.

c. **Cardiac** muscles make up the heart.

muscle injuries

d. A **cramp** is a "charley horse."

e. A **strain** is an overstretched muscle.

f. A **sprain** is a torn ligament.

Answers may include wearing proper equipment such as a helmet and cycling shoes; doing warm-up exercises before a ride and cool-down exercises after a ride; eating healthy foods; and getting enough rest before and after a ride.

Process Skills
Communicating

Suppose you joined a bicycle club that will be riding long distances. What precautions can you take to prepare for these rides? What can you do to avoid injury? Write your answer on a separate sheet of paper.

© Silver Burdett Ginn

Chapter Test
Bones and Muscles

CHAPTER 1

Name _____ Date _____

Analyze Information Each item is worth 10 points.

1. The pictures show how paired muscles work to bend and straighten your arms. What happens to the biceps and triceps muscles when the girl bends her elbow? Express your answer by labeling the arm muscles in the second diagram.

Biceps contracts
Triceps relaxes
Triceps contracts
Biceps relaxes

2. What are the three main functions of the skeletal system?
The three main functions are give the body shape and support, help the body move, and protect important organs such as the heart and lungs.

Problem Solving Each item is worth 14 points.

3. This is a closeup view of what it looks like inside the shoulder joint. Draw arrow(s) to show where the ligaments are.

4. How do the bones, ligaments, and cartilage of the shoulder joint shown work together?
Ligaments hold bones together at joints. Cartilage provides padding where the bones rub together.

5. How could you use clay and wire to model your ribs? What is the function of the ribs? Write or draw your answer on a separate sheet of paper.
The clay could be used to make the sternum and the spine. The wire (ribs) could be attached to the sternum and the spine and wrapped around to protect the organs in the rib cage.

© Silver Burdett Ginn

© Silver Burdett Ginn

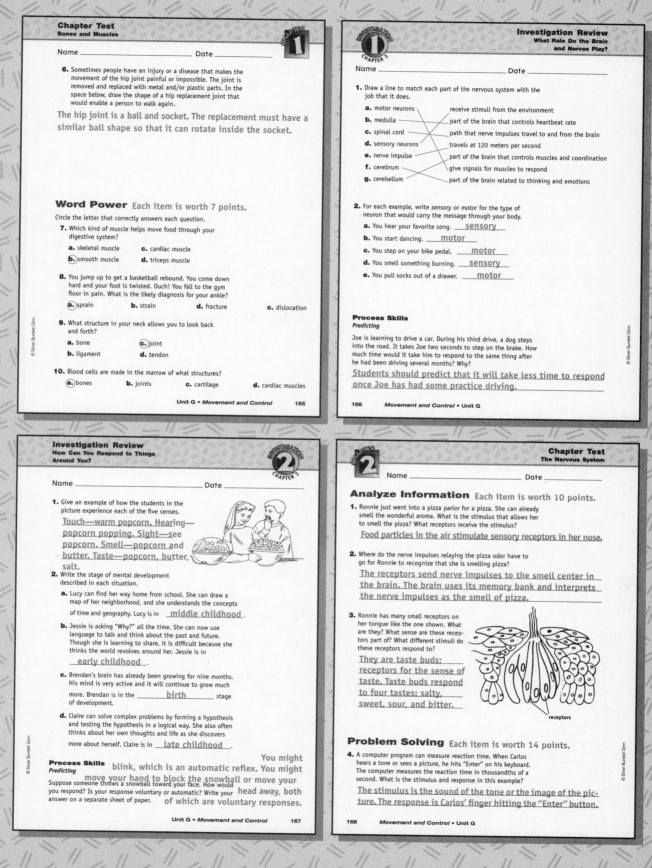

Chapter Test
Bones and Muscles

1

Name _____ Date _____

6. Sometimes people have an injury or a disease that makes the movement of the hip joint painful or impossible. The joint is removed and replaced with metal and/or plastic parts. In the space below, draw the shape of a hip replacement joint that would enable a person to walk again.

The hip joint is a ball and socket. The replacement must have a similar ball shape so that it can rotate inside the socket.

Word Power Each item is worth 7 points.

Circle the letter that correctly answers each question.

7. Which kind of muscle helps move food through your digestive system?
   a. skeletal muscle   c. cardiac muscle
   b. smooth muscle   d. triceps muscle

8. You jump up to get a basketball rebound. You come down hard and your foot is twisted. Ouch! You fall to the gym floor in pain. What is the likely diagnosis for your ankle?
   a. sprain   b. strain   d. fracture   c. dislocation

9. What structure in your neck allows you to look back and forth?
   a. bone   c. joint
   b. ligament   d. tendon

10. Blood cells are made in the marrow of what structures?
    a. bones   b. joints   c. cartilage   d. cardiac muscles

Unit G • Movement and Control   165

Investigation Review
What Role Do the Brain and Nerves Play?

INVESTIGATION 1 • CHAPTER 2

Name _____ Date _____

1. Draw a line to match each part of the nervous system with the job that it does.
   a. motor neurons — receive stimuli from the environment
   b. medulla — part of the brain that controls heartbeat rate
   c. spinal cord — path that nerve impulses travel to and from the brain
   d. sensory neurons — travels at 120 meters per second
   e. nerve impulse — part of the brain that controls muscles and coordination
   f. cerebrum — give signals for muscles to respond
   g. cerebellum — part of the brain related to thinking and emotions

2. For each example, write *sensory* or *motor* for the type of neuron that would carry the message through your body.
   a. You hear your favorite song. __sensory__
   b. You start dancing. __motor__
   c. You step on your bike pedal. __motor__
   d. You smell something burning. __sensory__
   e. You pull socks out of a drawer. __motor__

Process Skills
Predicting

Joe is learning to drive a car. During his third drive, a dog steps into the road. It takes Joe two seconds to step on the brake. How much time would it take him to respond to the same thing after he had been driving several months? Why?

Students should predict that it will take less time to respond once Joe has had some practice driving.

166   *Movement and Control • Unit G*

Investigation Review
How Can You Respond to Things Around You?

INVESTIGATION 2 • CHAPTER 2

Name _____ Date _____

1. Give an example of how the students in the picture experience each of the five senses.
   Touch—warm popcorn. Hearing—popcorn popping. Sight—see popcorn and butter. Taste—popcorn, butter, salt.

2. Write the stage of mental development described in each situation.
   a. Lucy can find her way home from school. She can draw a map of her neighborhood, and she understands the concepts of time and geography. Lucy is in __middle childhood__.
   b. Jessie is asking "Why?" all the time. She can now use language to talk and think about the past and future. Though she is learning to share, it is difficult because she thinks the world revolves around her. Jessie is in __early childhood__.
   c. Brendan's brain has already been growing for nine months. His mind is very active and it will continue to grow much more. Brendan is in the __birth__ stage of development.
   d. Claire can solve complex problems by forming a hypothesis and testing the hypothesis in a logical way. She also often thinks about her own thoughts and life as she discovers more about herself. Claire is in __late childhood__.

Process Skills
Predicting

Suppose someone throws a snowball toward your face. How would you respond? Is your response voluntary or automatic? Write your answer on a separate sheet of paper.

You might blink, which is an automatic reflex. You might move your hand to block the snowball or move your head away, both of which are voluntary responses.

Unit G • Movement and Control   167

Chapter Test
The Nervous System

2

Name _____ Date _____

Analyze Information Each item is worth 10 points.

1. Ronnie just went into a pizza parlor for a pizza. She can already smell the wonderful aroma. What is the stimulus that allows her to smell the pizza? What receptors receive the stimulus?
   Food particles in the air stimulate sensory receptors in her nose.

2. Where do the nerve impulses relaying the pizza odor have to go for Ronnie to recognize that she is smelling pizza?
   The receptors send nerve impulses to the smell center in the brain. The brain uses its memory bank and interprets the nerve impulses as the smell of pizza.

3. Ronnie has many small receptors on her tongue like the one shown. What are they? What sense are these receptors part of? What different stimuli do these receptors respond to?
   They are taste buds; receptors for the sense of taste. Taste buds respond to four tastes: salty, sweet, sour, and bitter.

receptors

Problem Solving Each item is worth 14 points.

4. A computer program can measure reaction time. When Carlos hears a tone or sees a picture, he hits "Enter" on his keyboard. The computer measures the reaction time in thousandths of a second. What is the stimulus and response in this example?
   The stimulus is the sound of the tone or the image of the picture. The response is Carlos' finger hitting the "Enter" button.

168   *Movement and Control • Unit G*

© Silver Burdett Ginn

Chapter Test
The Nervous System

CHAPTER 2

Name _____ Date _____

5. Have you ever played a guessing game where you blindfold a person and he or she identifies items in a bag by feeling them? Why is this possible?

The sensory receptors in the skin sense the stimuli from the objects and send this information along sensory neurons to the brain. The brain uses its memory bank to interpret the sensory impulses and create an image.

6. How well do you think you would be able to taste if you lost your sense of smell? Can you think of a time when this might happen temporarily?

Taste would be impaired because the sense of taste is a combination of nerve impulses from the taste buds and the receptors in the nose; when you have a bad cold and a stuffy nose you may lose your sense of taste.

Word Power Each item is worth 7 points.

Circle the letter of each correct answer.

7. Barry is thinking about a wish list for his birthday. He is using his ____ .
   a. cerebellum **b.** cerebrum c. medulla d. sensory cortex

8. A response that helps you protect your body is probably a ____ .
   a. heartbeat b. brain wave pattern c. motor neuron **d.** reflex

9. Information about sound vibrations is carried by nerve impulses along the ____ .
   a. optic nerve **b.** auditory nerve c. spinal cord d. retina

10. ____ are signals that start a nerve impulse.
   a. motor neurons c. auditory nerves
   b. stimuli d. brain waves

Unit G • Movement and Control   169

INVESTIGATION 1
CHAPTER 3

Investigation Review
How Do Drugs Affect the Body?

Name _____ Date _____

1. Match each term with its definition.

   a. addiction — drug found in coffee, chocolate, some teas, and some soft drinks
   b. nicotine — a group of drugs that can be legally purchased without a prescription
   c. caffeine — stimulant found in tobacco
   d. steroids — drugs that severely depress the nervous system and can cause death from overdose
   e. narcotics — drugs that act like the body's natural hormones
   f. over-the-counter drugs — dependency on a substance that makes it difficult to stop using it

2. Write each of the drugs listed in the correct column. Star the drugs that are illegal.

alcohol	cocaine	marijuana
amphetamines	heroin	nicotine
crack	LSD	tranquilizers

Stimulants	Depressants	Hallucinogens	Narcotics
amphetamines	alcohol	*marijuana	*heroin
cocaine, nicotine	tranquilizers	*LSD	
*crack			

Answers should reflect accurate information in a creative

Process Skills
Communicating

way. Any mixture not designed for medical use as an inhalant may contain compounds that can be poisonous.

Some paints, glues, office products, and cleansers contain toxins that can be harmful if inhaled. A single use of any of these substances can cause liver, kidney, or brain damage. On a separate sheet of paper, design an advertisement about the dangers of inhalants.

170   Movement and Control • Unit G

Investigation Review
How Does Alcohol Affect the Body?

INVESTIGATION 2
CHAPTER 3

Name _____ Date _____

1. Fill in the blanks using the terms in the box.

misused	deformed	heat	liver damage
blood system	depresses	judgment	mental illness

Some people may drink alcohol to relax, but alcohol can be dangerous when it is __misused__ . Unlike food, alcohol is absorbed by the __blood system__ quickly. Alcohol causes __heat__ loss, which makes the drinker feel colder. Alcohol also __depresses__ the nervous system, causing people to become slow and clumsy. Abused over a long time, alcohol can cause __mental illness__ , __liver damage__ , and heart disease. Sadly, if a pregnant woman drinks, her unborn child could be born __deformed__ or with severe damage to the nervous system. Alcohol impairs __judgment__ , and a person who drives while drinking can cause accidents.

2. Fill in the chart with the effects alcohol has on the human body.

Short-Term Effects	Long-Term Effects
expansion of blood vessels causing an increase in heart rate and blood pressure, heat loss and reddish color; impairment of brain functions	mental illness, liver disease, heart disease, and digestive system damage

Students' answers should reflect decision-making and communication skills that they have used in their debates about alcohol advertising.

Process Skills
Communicating, Making Decisions

You have just watched a sporting event on television and seen commercials for alcoholic beverages. You've decided to write a letter to the television network about the ads. On a separate sheet of paper list the main points you will make in your letter.

Unit G • Movement and Control   171

CHAPTER 3

Chapter Test
Staying in Control

Name _____ Date _____

Analyze Information Each item is worth 12 points.

For questions 1–4, circle the letter of the best answer.

1. Which of the following substances is absorbed directly into the bloodstream, depresses the nervous system, and causes long-term liver and heart disease?
   a. nicotine
   b. any drug
   c. alcohol
   d. caffeine

2. Which of the following is a fatal disease of the body's immune system that can be spread by improper use of needles?
   a. alcoholism
   b. AIDS
   c. addiction
   d. cancer

3. Drugs that act like hormones and can damage the heart and other organs are ____ .
   a. stimulants
   b. narcotics
   c. inhalants
   d. steroids

4. Marijuana, hashish, and LSD are all kinds of ____ , which can alter perception and awareness.
   a. stimulants
   b. hallucinogens
   c. depressants
   d. narcotics

172   Movement and Control • Unit G

·····Answers·····

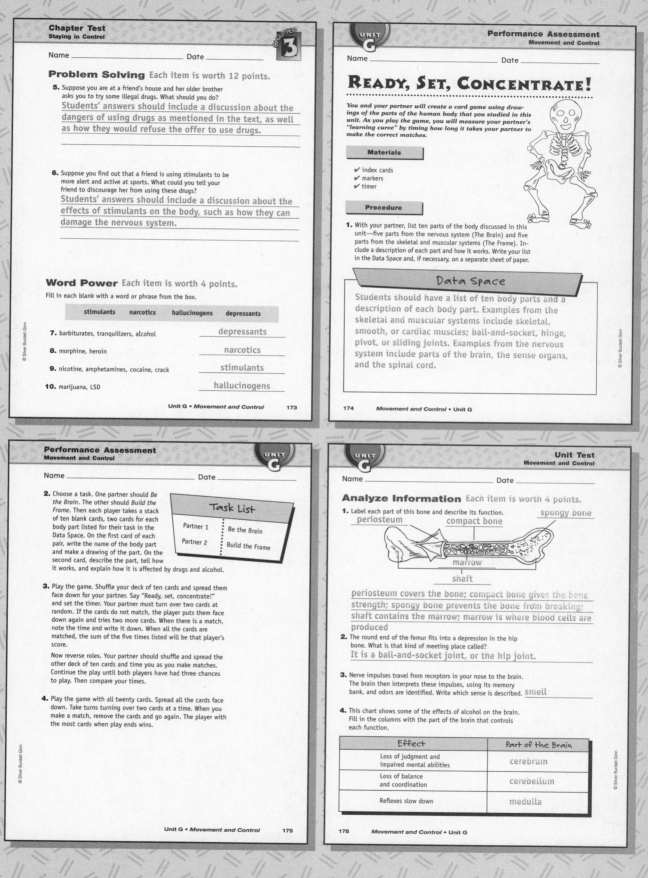

Chapter Test
Staying in Control

[CHAPTER 3]

Name _____ Date _____

Problem Solving Each item is worth 12 points.

5. Suppose you are at a friend's house and her older brother asks you to try some illegal drugs. What should you do?
   Students' answers should include a discussion about the dangers of using drugs as mentioned in the text, as well as how they would refuse the offer to use drugs.

6. Suppose you find out that a friend is using stimulants to be more alert and active at sports. What could you tell your friend to discourage her from using these drugs?
   Students' answers should include a discussion about the effects of stimulants on the body, such as how they can damage the nervous system.

Word Power Each item is worth 4 points.

Fill in each blank with a word or phrase from the box.

stimulants	narcotics	hallucinogens	depressants

7. barbiturates, tranquilizers, alcohol .... _depressants_

8. morphine, heroin .... _narcotics_

9. nicotine, amphetamines, cocaine, crack .... _stimulants_

10. marijuana, LSD .... _hallucinogens_

© Silver Burdett Ginn

Unit G • Movement and Control   173

[UNIT G]

Performance Assessment
Movement and Control

Name _____ Date _____

READY, SET, CONCENTRATE!

You and your partner will create a card game using drawings of the parts of the human body that you studied in this unit. As you play the game, you will measure your partner's "learning curve" by timing how long it takes your partner to make the correct matches.

Materials

✔ index cards
✔ markers
✔ timer

Procedure

1. With your partner, list ten parts of the body discussed in this unit—five parts from the nervous system (The Brain) and five parts from the skeletal and muscular systems (The Frame). Include a description of each part and how it works. Write your list in the Data Space and, if necessary, on a separate sheet of paper.

Data Space

Students should have a list of ten body parts and a description of each body part. Examples from the skeletal and muscular systems include skeletal, smooth, or cardiac muscles; ball-and-socket, hinge, pivot, or sliding joints. Examples from the nervous system include parts of the brain, the sense organs, and the spinal cord.

© Silver Burdett Ginn

174   Movement and Control • Unit G

Performance Assessment
Movement and Control

[UNIT G]

Name _____ Date _____

2. Choose a task. One partner should *Be the Brain.* The other should *Build the Frame.* Then each player takes a stack of ten blank cards, two cards for each body part listed for their task in the Data Space. On the first card of each pair, write the name of the body part and make a drawing of the part. On the second card, describe the part, tell how it works, and explain how it is affected by drugs and alcohol.

Task List	
Partner 1	Be the Brain
Partner 2	Build the Frame

3. Play the game. Shuffle your deck of ten cards and spread them face down for your partner. Say "Ready, set, concentrate!" and set the timer. Your partner must turn over two cards at random. If the cards do not match, the player puts them face down again and tries two more cards. When there is a match, note the time and write it down. When all the cards are matched, the sum of the five times listed will be that player's score.

   Now reverse roles. Your partner should shuffle and spread the other deck of ten cards and time you as you make matches. Continue the play until both players have had three chances to play. Then compare your times.

4. Play the game with all twenty cards. Spread all the cards face down. Take turns turning over two cards at a time. When you make a match, remove the cards and go again. The player with the most cards when play ends wins.

© Silver Burdett Ginn

Unit G • Movement and Control   175

[UNIT G]

Unit Test
Movement and Control

Name _____ Date _____

Analyze Information Each item is worth 4 points.

1. Label each part of this bone and describe its function.

   periosteum   compact bone   spongy bone
   marrow
   shaft

   periosteum covers the bone; compact bone gives the bone strength; spongy bone prevents the bone from breaking; shaft contains the marrow; marrow is where blood cells are produced

2. The round end of the femur fits into a depression in the hip bone. What is that kind of meeting place called?
   It is a ball-and-socket joint, or the hip joint.

3. Nerve impulses travel from receptors in your nose to the brain. The brain then interprets these impulses, using its memory bank, and odors are identified. Write which sense is described. _smell_

4. This chart shows some of the effects of alcohol on the brain. Fill in the columns with the part of the brain that controls each function.

Effect	Part of the Brain
Loss of judgment and impaired mental abilities	_cerebrum_
Loss of balance and coordination	_cerebellum_
Reflexes slow down	_medulla_

© Silver Burdett Ginn

178   Movement and Control • Unit G

© Silver Burdett Ginn

Unit Test
Movement and Control

Name _____ Date _____

Use the picture below to answer questions 5–8.

5. Label the stimulus, the sensory neurons, and the motor neurons in the picture.

motor neuron

stimulus

sensory neuron

6. What kind of message do the motor neurons send?

They send a message to the muscles of the arm that causes them to move the hand away from the hot object.

7. What pathway carries this impulse to the brain? When will the person know what has happened?

The spinal cord carries impulses to the brain. After the impulses are received, the person will know what happened.

8. Which sense receptors are receiving stimuli?

Receptors of pain and heat in the skin are receiving stimuli.

9. Kyle's dog sees Kyle throw a ball. The dog sees the ball, leaps, and snatches the ball in midair. What could you call the time it takes the dog to respond?

reaction time

Unit G • Movement and Control   179

Unit Test
Movement and Control

Name _____ Date _____

Problem Solving Each item is worth 8 points.

10. Suppose you are baby-sitting two 2-year-old children. They fight over the same toys and can't seem to share things. Why are they behaving like this? What might you do to help? Young children think the world revolves around them and have difficulty sharing. Students may suggest helping the children take turns, removing the most desirable toys, or changing the activity often.

11. Newborn babies are born with reflexes, which they outgrow. One of these is the stepping reflex. When held upright on a flat surface a newborn may lift one leg and then the other, as if taking steps. This is an involuntary reflex that disappears by about two months in order for the child to learn to walk. Explain why.

If the involuntary stepping reflex remained, the child would not need to learn the voluntary movement of walking.

12. You and your family enjoy going to a restaurant near your home, but it doesn't have a nonsmoking section. On a separate sheet of paper, write a letter stating the arguments you would use to convince the owners to make a nonsmoking section. Smoking is a factor in over 400,000 deaths in America each year; it can cause lung cancer and heart disease; nicotine can cause addiction; second-hand smoke can be dangerous.

13. The breath tester shows the results of a blood alcohol test given to a driver. Is the driver in trouble? Why or why not? Why are laws needed to regulate this problem?

In most states this driver is legally drunk because the blood alcohol concentration is over 0.1. Laws are necessary because of the high number of deaths attributed to drivers who were drinking alcohol.

180   Movement and Control • Unit G

Unit Test
Movement and Control

Name _____ Date _____

14. Suppose your school is having a Drug Awareness Week. What would you write on a poster to make others aware of the dangers of taking drugs?

Answers should show understanding of drugs and their dangers.

Word Power Each item is worth 4 points.
Circle the letter of the word or words to complete each sentence.

15. Bones are joined to bones by ____.
 a. cartilage   **c.** ligaments
 b. tendons   d. periosteum

16. Muscles damaged in a heart attack are ____ muscles.
 a. cardiac   c. skeletal
 b. smooth   d. biceps

17. Heat, cold, pressure, and pain are stimuli sensed by ____.
 a. light receptors   **c.** touch receptors
 b. auditory receptors d. smell receptors

18. Sounds are vibrations that travel through the ear canal and eardrum to the inner ear, where they become nerve impulses moving to the brain along the ____.
 a. auditory nerve c. optic nerve
 b. brainwaves   d. taste buds

19. Nicotine and caffeine are commonly used ____.
 a. depressants   c. narcotics
 b. stimulants   d. steroids

20. A substance that is difficult to stop using is said to be ____.
 a. an over-the-counter drug   c. a prescription drug
 b. addictive   d. a steroid

Unit G • Movement and Control   181

© Silver Burdett Ginn